KYLIAN MBAPPE

The Golden Boy

No part of this book may be reproduced or transmitted in any form or by any means, electronic or mechanical, including photocopying, recording, or by any information storage or retrieval system, without written permission from Sole Books. For information regarding permission write to Sole Books, P.O. Box 10445, Beverly Hills, CA 90213.

Editor: Y. Ginsberg

Proof editor: Marc Murphy-Robinson

Cover and layout design: Lazar Kackarovski

Cover picture: AP Photo/Thibault Camus

Library of Congress Cataloging-in-Publication data available.

Print ISBN: 978-1-938591-82-2
eBook ISBN: 978-1-938591-83-9

Published by Sole Books, an imprint of Wild Soccer USA, Beverly Hills, California.

Printed in the United States of America.

First edition.

www.solebooks.com

Kylian Mbappe

The Golden Boy

by
Kevin Ashby and Michael Part

More in the Soccer Stars Series:

www.solebooks.com

CHAPTER ONE

It's in His Genes

Five-year-old Kylian Mbappe Lottin held a tennis ball under his big toe. Just ahead, between him and the shelves in the living room, was his father's imitation leather armchair. In Kylian's imagination, it was the dominating figure of Italian goalkeeper Gianluigi Buffon, considered one of the best in the world. Behind him, a low table piled with old, well-read magazines stood for the Italian back four. In his mind, he had just dribbled past them. This was his last chance to win the World Cup for France.

Quick as lightning – so fast even Kylian's mother, Fayza, standing in the kitchen door, couldn't see – Kylian pinged the tennis ball up in the air and lashed it on its way. It rocketed toward the very middle of the armchair.

Surely Buffon's huge hands would stop the shot.

Not this time.

At the last moment, just as Kylian planned, the ball swerved up and to the left, as if on a string. It flew straight over the chair into the shelves, smashing the framed print of Mom and Dad's wedding, which crashed onto the floor.

"Gooo-al!" Kylian shouted. "Mbappe wins the World Cup trophy!"

"KYLIAN!" Fayza's yell shattered the boy's fantasy.

She was towering over him, her dark eyes on fire with a look that was equal parts exasperation and laughter.

"That was the memory of the second-best day of my life! Pick it up!"

Kylian blinked and looked at the wedding photo on the floor, the frame twisted and covered in shards of glass.

"Now, little Pelé!"

Kylian trotted behind his dad's chair and lifted the frame off the floor. He tried to straighten it, then put it back on the shelf where it listed like a rowboat in a storm. He smiled at his mother.

"Sorry," he said.

He outstretched his arms, and Fayza pulled his coat on around him. They hadn't been able to keep his feet still since he could walk. If it wasn't an actual ball, it was a sock or a scrunched-up wad of paper.

They lived in Bondy, a suburb of Paris, France. Fayza used to be a champion handball player, and Kylian's dad, Wilfrid, once played for Bondy Football Club and was now the club's youth coach. *The kid has good genes*, Fayza thought. She looked at her watch.

"Come on," she called, thrusting him through the front door. "We'll be late to the match."

Kylian took the stairs two at a time.

As soon as they hit the pavement, he dropped the soccer ball onto his left boot and flipped it over Fayza's head, then set off dancing past passers-by as if they were trying to win possession.

"Careful!" his mom said, but it was too late.

"I am!" Kylian said, frowning, and kicked the ball with remarkable force. The ball soared over the cars and smashed into the display of fruits and vegetables at the front of the small market across the street, spilling yams, tomatoes, greens, and onions onto the ground.

Fayza's eyes widened. Then she rushed between the cars as fast as she could, pushing Kylian in front of her, and apologizing to the drivers who honked at them as they crossed the road.

"Put them back," she ordered Kylian, pulling her purse out of her bag. Mr. Kembo, the grocer, appeared at his door. He was from Cameroon in Africa, like Kylian's dad.

"I'm so sorry," she began. "Please let me pay."

Kylian's face was red as he bent down. Mr. Kembo just laughed.

"Fayza, that son of yours has a shot like a cannon." He waved away the ten-euro note Fayza tried to press into his hands. "No harm done." He picked a burst tomato off the pavement and bit into it. "Nothing's spoiled."

"I-I'm sorry, Mr. Kembo," Kylian muttered without prompting.

"Your punishment will be..." Mr. Kembo began, and Kylian's eyes widened. He didn't like to be punished. "... to hit the ball like that for PSG." Mr. Kembo grinned.

"Actually, that will be every other team's punishment," he said and laughed at his own joke.

They were both avid Paris St. Germain fans.

Kylian grinned. "I'll play for PSG one day."

Fayza raised an eyebrow.

"First, put the tomatoes in a bag," she said. Kylian obeyed and handed her the bag. She handed it to Mr. Kembo. "I'll take them. I need some for pasta."

She turned to Kylian. "And from you, I'll take the football."

CHAPTER TWO

The Mascot

At Bondy's training pitch, Kylian saw his brother, Jirès, and his friends Fabian and José shooting a ball toward the goal.

"Three against one, I will beat you!" Kylian chirped. He dropped the net of balls and got one onto his right foot, keepy-uppy style. The boys tried hard not to laugh.

"No!" Jirès said. "You are too young!"

"We'll go easy," Fabian said, smirking.

The ball was instantly at Kylian's feet. The other boys were twice his size. His eyes shone. He'd show them!

First, he danced on the spot, then he spooned the ball onto his instep and sent it in a perfect line between his opponents. He sped after it. Fabian moved to intercept, but Kylian swerved nimbly by and got to the ball first. He aimed a shot, and the back of the goal ballooned.

"Mbappe, the hero from Bondy, scores again!" he carolled.

Rushing to the ball, he scooped it up and ran back to the edge of the penalty area.

The older boys hung back, spreading arms and legs wide as Kylian began trotting toward them. Kylian sized the situation up with a quick look – and sent the ball curving above them into the right-hand corner of the goal.

"That's two to nothing," he said.

"Not for long!" José said.

Kylian didn't get another chance. His dad arrived with a dozen more boys and a stack of cones.

"I am beating them!" Kylian announced proudly.

"Well done," his dad said. "But now it's time for some real practice." He pointed at the sidelines.

It was so disappointing! Kylian nodded and went slowly to the edge of the field. He watched his father put the team through warm-ups, passing drills, and dribbling work with the cones. He wished he could join in. His feet itched, but his dad didn't look in his direction once.

After an hour, Wilfrid called all the youth players together.

"OK guys, pair off. I want to practice free kicks with you," he began. "One of you places the ball on the spot, the other comes from left or right and makes a dummy-shot. Then the first one kicks the ball. Five times, then change positions. To keep the goalie alert, sometimes the dummy shooter will actually shoot. Got that?"

The boys looked confused, but they said nothing. Kylian, however, thought it was obvious. He wanted to try it.

"Right. Fabian, José, you're the first pair. Everyone else, make a wall."

Kylian watched, frustrated, as one-by-one the boys kicked the ball and the wall of the other boys blocked the shots. Everyone but Fabian, who made every shot. Kylian thought he was going to explode. "Dad! Let me play!"

Wilfred gave him a look. "No," he said. "You are too young to play on the team."

Although he'd heard it before, Kylian looked as if he was going to cry.

"Hey, Mr. Mbappe," José said unexpectedly. "You should give him a chance. I'll be his partner."

Wilfrid gave José a look.

"He's right," Fabian chimed in. "After what he did to us while we were waiting for you, I'd like to see him get a chance to do it again. In a real match."

Wilfrid stared at Kylian, then nodded slowly.

"Score, and I'll let you be the team's mascot."

Kylian charged onto the field before Wilfred could say another word.

The first time, he faked so expertly that even José was fooled and forgot to shoot. The second time, he pinged one off his right boot and put all his effort into it. It was a full-size ball, not the smaller size ball he'd played with earlier. It didn't fly, but it did swerve in the air and lift off the ground. The keeper wasn't expecting anything, and it bounced into the back of the net. Wilfrid's expression didn't change. The third shot was another fake. The fourth found a sweet spot on Kylian's boot and sang past the keeper's outstretched fingers.

Wilfrid tried hard not to smile, but the boys whooped Kylian's name. The keeper shook his head, smiling.

That night, Wilfrid and Fayza sat in the kitchen while Kylian was in his room, playing FIFA PlayStation. Fayza told him what had happened at the fruit store.

"He needs some real goals, Wil," she said. "Some training structure to burn off all that extra energy."

"He whipped half a dozen balls past Alain today," Wilfrid mused.

"He told me," Fayza said. "Maybe he's ready."

Wilfrid chuckled. "The day he turns six, we'll start him at Bondy."

Fayza smiled at her husband. "Go tell him."

Wilfred got up and strolled into Kylian's bedroom.

Half a minute later, Kylian's shouts of joy sent the birds flying all over Paris.

CHAPTER THREE

Father and Son

Kylian loped ahead of his father as they came out onto the junior training pitches. He'd been at Bondy for three months now, and he'd loved every minute of it. Today was going to be the best yet.

"Théo, Joe, Metehan," he yelled to his three best pals.

They gave each other reverse finger handshakes, giggling.

"Guess what!" Kylian enthused. "Jirès is coming today."

Jirès had trained with the Bondy youth team when he first arrived in France and stayed with Mom and Dad, who adopted him before Kylian was born. After that, he'd gone to live at the Clairefontaine Football Academy, where the French Football Federation developed their young talented kids. Jirès already had a contract at Rennes, a top division club near France's northwest coast.

"He'll watch us," Kylian carried on. "Maybe even join in."

"Awesome!" Théo said. He liked playing in goal, though he could also play midfield.

"He's coming to play for Bondy."

"He can't play for Bondy! He's got a contract. He's just visiting."

"Well, he used to play here!"

"Boys!" Wilfrid bellowed before Kylian could continue the argument. "Line up. In pairs. Facing each other."

Kylian groaned. He just wanted to play.

Wilfrid made the boys jog up and down around each other, then do stretches. It felt like forever, but he finally got the balls out and training began.

Wilfrid set up cones in parallel rows close to the center line. He made the boys take the ball forward along the line, then pass to a boy opposite when they got to the end. That boy would then come down the cones. It was a basic control drill, but still tricky. Wilfrid made them use full-size balls, so it was harder. Gradually, he increased the speed.

"Not too far in front of you," he warned. "Your opponent could sneak in."

And not so close or you'll miss your stride, Kylian thought.

Soon, it was his turn to come back down the line. He concentrated hard – Dad always judged his technique ruthlessly. More so than the rest. He was determined to be perfect.

His first punt sent the ball past the first cone, ten yards away. Kylian strained to keep up, reaching it just as it began to lose momentum. So far, so good. He gave the ball a touch to push it on. Not quite hard enough – it fell to his left foot when he caught up and he had to check to steer it ahead.

Wilfrid clapped at him to keep the pace up.

Dad never called him "son" when they were on the training pitch – just his name.

By the time Kylian reached the third cone, his run was back on track. Grunting with the effort of directing the heavier ball, he poked it in a perfect stride. Level with the last cone, he looked up and side-footed it invitingly to Théo, who had come on too quickly. The ball went off course.

Dad was already watching Théo. And frowning.

Kylian scuttled to the back of the line. Théo was a good friend, but Kylian knew he was a much better player. Théo made it to the end of the cones, but he goofed more than once and sprayed the ball a bit.

"Try taking it a little easier," Wilfrid told him.

At the back of the line, Kylian sighed.

"Nice work, little bro." He smiled.

"Jirès!"

His tall, slim brother knocked his shoulder playfully.

"I made a mistake on the second cone," Kylian replied, then wished he hadn't said it.

"You'll clean that up next time." Jirès shrugged.

Kylian giggled. "Are you going to play?"

"Maybe. I'll take goal."

Jirès gave Kylian a high-five, then strode over to Wilfrid. Kylian glowed inside.

The next exercise was dribbling. Kylian loved it. Dad took the stopwatch out and timed their runs. Kylian pushed himself, trying to make each run count. With Jirès there, he wanted to impress him. Adrenaline rushed through him. When the exercise finished, Jirès gave him a thumbs-up. Even Wilfrid nodded.

They ended the session with a nine-a-side match. Jirès in goal. While they picked sides, Mr. Fanfan, Théo's dad, who coached the next age group, came over and said he'd take the other goal. Wilfrid picked Kylian last, on Jirès's team, then blew the whistle.

All Kylian wanted was to get the ball, dodge down the field, and score. He made constant runs into space and called. If that didn't work, he scampered and took the ball from deep, ghosting past his friends as if they weren't there.

Suddenly, he saw Dad looking at his watch and making to blow his whistle to end the game.

No!

Hurriedly, he called out to Jirès, who'd just saved a good shot from Joe. The ball landed at his feet, and he took off like lightning.

One stride. Two.

Joe, who was back-tracking, lunged close to the ball, but Kylian dinked it past him.

Three. Four.

Metehan approached – he was the best tackler and knew how to time his moves better. Kylian stalled in front of him, feinting left, right, left. Then there was a gap between Metehan's feet. Kylian nutmegged him and sprinted forward.

Two more tried to intercept. Kylian passed them both at lightning speed. Now it was just Mr. Fanfan filling the goal.

Kylian looked him in the eye and lined up his shot. As he expected, the coach started to come off his line, narrowing the angle. In the blink of an eye, Kylian changed tack, reined the ball in, and dribbled it past the coach, then side-footed it into the empty net.

He stood, hands on hips, satisfied, as Wilfrid's whistle sounded.

Later that night, as he played FIFA 2006 in bed, he heard Jirès giggling from the living room.

"The look on Fanfan's face!"

Mom hugged Ethan, Kylian's new baby brother.

"I had to let Kylian run," Wilfrid agreed. "He looked so happy. So absorbed. You know Fayza, Fanfan thinks Kylian should go up to the Under-Tens. I think I agree."

"He'll look like a pixie," Fayza laughed. "But why not? He's ten times better than anyone else you've coached."

Jirès nodded in agreement.

"I know," Wilfrid said quietly. Then he laughed. "You should have seen it, Fayza. Fanfan had egg all over his face!"

CHAPTER FOUR

The Under-Tens

Kylian ran as fast as he could down the school corridor, flute in hand. Lessons were over for the day, but he still had his daily review. Mom's insistence. His form teacher, Mark, and the headmaster, Mr. Saint-Aubert, sat down with her to report how he'd behaved. He didn't like it. Then again, he figured he deserved it. School was a bore compared to soccer. All he was trying to do was make it more fun.

Like now.

He got to the form room before the adults and quickly laid his bags on his desk. Then he squeezed into the supply closet and closed the door until there was only a crack. Soft as a whisper, he blew into the flute. It sounded like the howling wind.

A minute later, Mr. Saint-Aubert and Mark came in, laughing. Mom followed. Ethan, who was one now, was perched on Mark's shoulders. They saw the bags and looked around.

"Where's Kylian?" Mom cooed to Ethan. "Where can he be?"

Ethan giggled.

"Maybe he had to go to the bathroom," Mom joked.

Ethan giggled louder.

Kylian raised the flute to his lips and blew.

Ethan squealed.

"Kylian!" Mom called. Kylian played a ghostly tune.

Putting a finger over her lips, Fayza tiptoed over to the cupboard.

"Boo!" Kylian exploded before she could reveal him. She couldn't help squealing. Kylian played a fun little ditty in response.

"Come on, you children of Bond – y – a," he shrilled to the tune of the French national anthem, marching into the classroom, twirling his flute.

Ethan giggled hysterically.

"Enough! Enough!" Fayza said, laughing along with her boys. "If this is you all day, I already know what your teachers are going to say!"

Kylian stopped in front of her, flute at his lips.

She pointed a slender finger toward the desks. "Get to your desk!" Then she threw her arms in the air as if she was giving up, maintaining her grin.

"I got you!" Kylian beamed. "Admit it!"

"I'll get you back, twerp," she replied, hands on hips. Then she turned to Mark. "How were his marks today?"

"Not bad. B in composition and math."

Fayza hummed. "He give you any trouble?"

Kylian shifted. Hopefully, the joke he'd played on the music teacher hadn't got back yet.

Mr. Saint-Aubert pulled a small whoopie cushion from his pocket and put it on Kylian's chair. Kylian's ears went red. It was his and designed to make rude noises.

"Have a seat," he said, his eyes narrowing.

"Gee, sir, I've been sitting all day, sir," Kylian began.

"SIT!" Mom ordered.

Giving up the fight, Kylian slowly sat down. As his weight settled, the cushion wheezed and squeaked and exploded with the sound of a perfectly formed fart. Everyone cracked up.

Even Ethan, who burst into peals of baby laughter.

Two hours later, everyone was piling into Fayza's car to go to Bondy stadium. These days, home was no longer just down the street.

For all his playfulness at school, Kylian was deadly serious now. He had a match. He fidgeted in the front seat as they wove through the suburbs. Dad glanced over at him.

"Take some deep breaths, son."

Kylian scowled. They were going to play a derby match against Stade de l'Est Under-Tens. They *had* to win. How could anyone be calm?

"For God's sake, try not to do everything on your own this time," Mom called out from the back seat.

"What if we're losing?" Kylian protested. "I won't be able to help it!"

"Trust your teammates," Uncle Pierre said. "Don't hog the ball!"

"Easier said than done," Mom said under her breath, and they all chuckled.

All but Kylian.

"Pierre's right," Dad chipped in. "If you hog the ball, no one will want to pass to you – and then you'll lose, anyway."

Kylian narrowed his eyes, annoyed. It was true that sometimes the other guys got mad when he didn't pass to them. But if they made a good run, he *always* passed. And as soon as he scored – which was *also always* – everyone was happy. Why couldn't they just let him be?

"OK, Dad. Will do," he said, but he didn't really mean it.

Uncle Pierre reached a hand over the seat onto Kylian's shoulder.

"Bondy will win, Kylian, don't worry."

And I'll do it my way, Kylian thought.

At half-time, the two teams were tied with no goals scored. Kylian was tense. Everything was wrong. Nothing was working out.

"Boys, we're playing well," Mr. Fanfan said to the huddle. "Théo, great save. Joe, good work in midfield. What we need now is to exploit their weaknesses and play to our strengths. Where are they falling down?"

Kylian put up his hand. When no one else responded, Mr. Fanfan nodded at him.

"Coach, they're narrow on the attack and have too many in the midfield."

"Do you see that?" Fanfan said, addressing the others. They looked back expectantly. "Go on, Kylian."

"Well, so we need to go wide, make runs behind and send in crosses," Kylian went on. "And we should defend further up. I think."

One of the boys looked angry.

"Kylian's right," Fanfan said firmly. "But he forgot one thing. We're a good passing team. At the moment, we're trying too hard. Let the ball do more work. Take your time. Slow the pace."

He paused.

"Especially you, Kylian!"

Kylian sighed. "I'll try."

"Trying doesn't cut it," Fanfan said.

Kylian looked at his feet, then looked up, and their eyes met. He nodded. "Yes, sir."

"Good," Fanfan clapped. "Let's do it!"

But the first thing that happened in the second half was a disaster. Stade de l'Est put a long ball up into the Bondy box, and Metehan tripped and touched the ball with his right hand as he went to intercept. The ref whistled and pointed to the penalty spot.

They buried the penalty.

"Don't panic!" Kylian called out to Joe as they placed the ball on the center circle for the restart. "Remember what Mr. Fanfan said. Play it wide but don't rush. I'll get in behind."

Joe listened. He combined with Metehan and found himself on the left with only the goalie in the box. Kylian timed a run, controlled Joe's cross, and bundled it home.

From then on, it was like a training run, with Kylian at the heart of everything. His second goal finished a surging dribble from halfway, helped by Joe's decoy. The hat-trick came from a free kick at the edge of the box. Between his own goals, he played Metehan in from the right sideline and lobbed the charging Stade de l'Est keeper for Joe to tap in.

Five-one. When the final whistle blew, the team danced jubilantly in the center of the pitch.

The opposition coach shook hands with Fanfan. "Your boy Kylian Mbappe," he said. "I heard about him – but that was something else. How does a boy his age know so much?"

"You should meet his mom and dad," Fanfan said with a grin.

CHAPTER FIVE

The Tremblay Tournament

Kylian was feverish with excitement. Bondy Under-Tens were going across Paris to Tremblay to play in an International Youth Tournament. F.C. Porto would be there. Feyenoord, too. Foreign teams. Top-flight clubs.

Jirès would be there too.

Kylian scanned the posters of his idols on his bedroom wall.

Cristiano Ronaldo... Ronaldinho... Zinedine Zidane – their eyes focused ahead, bodies feinting, the ball inches from their feet ready to hit its target. They were the first things Kylian looked at when he woke up and the last things he saw at night. On FIFA PlayStation, he could feel their moves in his own body, hear their encouragement. *You can do it, Kylian.*

Not long ago, he'd bounded into the hairdressers down the road and asked them to do his hair in a Zidane cut. Mom and Dad never let him forget it. Nor did his team.

"You think being bald is some kind of special haircut? Are your brains only in your feet?"

He didn't care what they said. Looking like Zidane was like being him – nothing else mattered. He wanted the spirit he had in his soccer. His game in his own.

He looked at the clock on the wall.

Only five in the morning and their new apartment was quiet. *Two hours* before anyone got up. He couldn't stand it. He pulled his tracksuit over his green and black Bondy kit, grabbed a ball, and tiptoed out of the house.

Everything was quiet on the street. There were birds in the fruit trees and willows behind the garden walls, but they weren't making the loud noise they did when the sun came up. He skipped along the pavement, keeping the ball in the air. He liked the new neighborhood – it was always peaceful – but he preferred having only one street to cross to get to a soccer field. At least there was the school. It was open on Saturday mornings for extra classes, and the caretaker never minded if he was there before the kids arrived. He'd practice against the wall for an hour. Get the tension out of his body.

The ball pinged off the brickwork, sounding like a penny dropping into a piggy bank. He chased back and forth, chipping, honing his shots, sometimes leaping up to control the ball. He grew calm and steady.

On the way home, he stopped at the bakery for a bag of fresh almond and chocolate croissants – Jirès's favorite.

His big brother was already sitting at the breakfast table when he came through the door, drinking a big mug of coffee. He, Dad, and Uncle Pierre were talking about the PSG game the previous night.

"Thank God for Clement equalizing," Jirès said. "I'd hate to be on a team that lost such a great record."

PSG had never been out of League One, but they'd flirted with relegation all season, which meant they were almost moved down to a lower tier of teams.

"Morning Kylian," Dad said, flashing a smile. He saw the powdered sugar on his son's face. "Couldn't wait?"

"Sorry," Kylian replied. "I just got some croissants for Jirès."

"Kissing up to me with croissants always works!" Jirès drawled. "What are you up to?"

"I'm thinking about the tournament!" Kylian said. "I want to win!"

Uncle Pierre smiled, holding his hand out for a croissant. "Make sure you do!"

Kylian blushed and gave his uncle the warm croissant he'd been hoping to gobble down himself. It's better to give than to receive. A lesson taught by his uncle himself.

Feyenoord Under-Tens were a goal up, but Bondy made a game of it. The Dutch team had kept all the possession at first, going two-zero before the match was twenty minutes old. They'd used their physical advantage, getting both goals from headers. The Parisians were getting desperate. Metehan lunged too hard with a tackle, earning a yellow card and nearly costing them a third goal.

It's about time, Kylian thought.

When he collected the ball in the Bondy box, he kept it. He didn't rush upfield, didn't make a dribbling exhibition, though he was tempted. The team needed calm. They needed to believe. And they need to control the ball. He passed, making himself available for the return. When it came, he advanced forward, then brought another teammate into the game. The Feyenoord midfield bore down, but Kylian ran cleverly, showing with his eyes where to pass.

One of the tall Dutch defenders tried to intimidate him. Kylian grinned. One skip and he was off, past the player and side-footing deftly to Joe. Joe surveyed the space ahead and saw nothing was on, so he played it back.

Good. That was the way. And they still had plenty of time.

Bondy got their first just before half-time, after Kylian took a short corner, ran hard at the box, and threaded a pass to the far post for Joe.

By halfway through the second period, Kylian's determination took over. The whole Bondy team had responded to his leadership. In possession, they kept the Feyenoord boys on the move, tiring them. When they lost the ball, they pressed, cramping the Dutch, cutting off the aerial route.

At last, their moment came.

Joe took off down the left, made it behind the Feyenoord defense, and sent a teasing cross hanging over the six-yard line. Kylian feinted a belter, and the Dutch players bought it. Metehan, up from deep, had a simple side-foot into the net.

The team rushed in for hugs and high-fives. Kylian felt fantastic. He smiled wide and looked for his family in the stands. They were waving like crazy.

All tournament, it was the same. Always Kylian in the middle of the action. Sometimes he dazzled, sometimes he kept everything clinical. He never yelled, and he never panicked. The team flowed, with him at its heart.

On the sideline, Fanfan nodded and smiled.

"Much better than all that showboating," Wilfrid said with a grin after the game. Uncle Pierre nodded.

"They could do with someone like him at PSG," Jirès observed. "Or in Rennes."

Fanfan chimed in. "The boy's only nine years old. If he's consistent, the scouts will hear about him soon enough."

"He thinks they should have already," Fayza said.

"Of course, he does," Wilfred said.

CHAPTER SIX

Mr. Hammache

It was an icy day, but the stands were full. It had been like that since the season kicked off. Strangers, as well as families. Not just to watch Kylian – Joe and Metehan had reputations of their own. Théo's dad, Fanfan, liked to watch too. Théo played in goal these days.

Mr. Ricardi, the Under-Thirteens coach, encouraged the Bondy team.

"The boys we're playing will work hard, but they don't have our skills. We can pull them around. Make gaps."

He glanced at Kylian. No need to motivate *him*. He was ready to go. He had a distant, slightly glassy look that only meant one thing when it came to Kylian: he was absolutely focused.

Kylian grinned back. Mr. Ricardi knew just how to handle him. No technical tips, just commentary. Ideas about decision-making. Things to try. It was like having a second pair of eyes. Mr. Ricardi noticed things, and his judgment was good.

"The pitch is like concrete today, sir," Kylian said.

Mr. Ricardi nodded.

"So the ball will zip around," Kylian went on, looking at his teammates. "We might take a few minutes to adapt, but it'll be OK."

Although he was playing above his age grade again, and all the boys were bigger than him, they took notice.

"Don't be scared of it," Ricardi agreed. "You can do this. OK, boys. And don't forget. Faster, higher, stronger!"

It was the Bondy motto. And Kylian's three favorite words.

The boys gathered in a circle, fists touching, and roared the words.

As they waited in their positions for the whistle, a small man with a mustache came and stood next to Mr. Ricardi. The coach obviously knew him – the two men shook hands. Then they settled in to watch the game.

The first half was slow and messy. The ball kept skipping on the freezing surface, just as Kylian had predicted, ricocheting knee-high instead of keeping close to the turf. Kylian mastered it quickly, stepping high to keep the ball under control, getting on his toes, but the others weren't as fast as him. It didn't help that the opposition was as aggressive as they come and Bondy couldn't impose themselves the way they usually did. The opponents clearly knew all about Kylian and were prepared to face him. They double-teamed him and hung off whenever he got the ball, as if afraid to commit to a tackle and find the little man leaving them behind. From the sideline, Fanfan – free to be just a supporter – bellowed support for every touch.

It was a frustrated group that clustered around Mr. Ricardi at half-time. Fanfan joined them.

"They're strangling our game," Jonathan Ikome complained. He played on the opposite wing to Kylian.

"I have an idea," Fanfan said. "Ricardi, may I?"

He winked at the coach and the man with the mustache. Kylian wondered if Fanfan knew him too.

"Boys, there's nothing to worry about. In the second half, just give Kylian the ball. They're scared of him!"

Everyone laughed. But Ricardi nodded. "OK! Showtime!"

Kylian grinned.

The second half was like watching a highlights reel.

Kylian roamed wherever there was space. When he found some, the Bondy boys mustered all their skill to deliver the ball. Passes flowed – across, back, across, forward – everyone helping one another out. Kylian collected and drove at the opposition, side-stepping, nutmegging, dinking, teasing. It was as if he'd given the ball a brain. The other team even tried to foul him, but it was no good. Kylian saw it coming and made use of being smaller to slither and duck and weave away from their studs and arms. Always, the ball twinkled in front of him like a magic trick, ready for the next prod from his caressing feet.

He waltzed in his first, then rocketed a low screamer from the edge of the box for number two.

His hat-trick was a balletic volley.

Goal number four came from an Ikome header after Kylian drew the whole opposing team to his wing only to lift a majestic cross.

The man with a mustache scribbled furiously on a notepad, smiling to himself. At the end of the match, everyone gathered around Kylian, laughing and cheering as he stood with one foot on the ball in a superman pose.

The stranger strode onto the pitch toward them. Kylian assumed he was some kind of reporter. That was fine. He practiced speeches all the time. When the man thrust out his hand, Kylian got ready for the questions.

"The buzz about you didn't lie," the stranger began. "That was an exceptional performance."

"Thank you," Kylian replied, his smile dazzling.

"I'm Reda Hammache," the man said. "I scout for your brother's team and a couple of others. I want you to come to try out for Rennes."

Kylian stared dumbly at him for the longest time. "B-but I just turned twelve," he managed.

Hammache grinned. "What's your point?"

Kylian stared back again. "I don't know".

"How about I tell you?" Hammache said.

"OK," Kylian said.

"You're good. We want you. Of course, only if your mom and dad agree," Hammache said. He stretched his hand for another shake.

Kylian grasped Hammache's hand tight and shook.

At home that night, everyone was talking and shouting at once.

"Rennes is a good club!"

"This is the beginning. A first chance."

"But you won't be top dog, Kylian," Dad said. "You'll have to work hard."

Kylian felt light-headed, as if he was taking off and floating.

"I'll play in front of Mr. Hammache," he said, the words spilling out uncontrollably. "I'll go to Clairefontaine just like Jirès. A big-shot club will spot me. Maybe PSG. Maybe Real Madrid. Zidane will see me! Free tickets to the Bernabéu, Uncle Pierre, for you and everyone. I promise!"

"That's quite a dream!" Fayza said.

Kylian settled down for a second. "You're right." He looked suddenly glum.

"But dreams can come true," Uncle Pierre said. "Happens all the time."

"Really?" Kylian said. "Can I tell you a secret?"

"All of us?" Fayza said. "It won't be much of a secret."

"It doesn't matter," Kylian replied and took a deep breath. "I'm going to win the World Cup. And bring it to Bondy."

Dad grinned, then leaned close to his son and put his arm around his shoulder. "I believe you, son. You have a gift. But work as if you didn't."

Kylian listened intently as his father spoke.

"Then anything can happen."

CHAPTER SEVEN

Gif-sur-Yvette

Sometimes his younger brother Ethan was the worst. For a whole hour and a half, he badgered Kylian – through the tree-lined early morning Bondy streets, onto the Paris circular *autoroute*, past the airport.

"Who's your PlayStation favorite?"

"Ronaldo." *Obviously.*

"I want to play against you."

"When you're older." *Like, never,* he thought.

"Show me how you curl a shot."

"Your feet are too small, squirt."

On and on and on.

Kylian needed to concentrate. Ever since Mr. Hammache had seen him play in February, he'd woken up every day thinking *today Rennes will call.* Finally, a month ago, an email had come. Mom read it out loud to him. They wanted him in a scratch team of hopefuls in May, in a place called Gif-sur-Yvette on the outskirts of Paris. Apparently, that was how they did things. Mr. Hammache would coach for the whole weekend, then they'd play some other teams.

Hammache counted. He was a former pro. Today and tomorrow counted.

"Mom," Kylian pleaded. "I need quiet!"

"Go on your PlayStation, Ethan," Fayza ordered, then turned up the car stereo. The music was his mom and dad's usual compilation playlist of African pop – Angelique Kidjo, Youssouf N'dour, Salif Keita. Kylian liked French rap better, but at least the music wasn't as aggravating as Ethan.

He started going through his signature moves in his head, flexing his muscles, breathing.

The pitches at Gif-sur-Yvette were right behind the town hall, surrounded by a lake and woods. There were dog-walkers and couples and what looked like hundreds of kids Kylian's age, with their parents. Mr. Hammache collected Kylian and about a dozen others with a sweep of his arm. Kylian recognized some of them – guys he'd played against – but most were strangers. He felt nervy and excited. He wanted to get going. He wanted to prove himself.

As soon as they started playing, he made a beeline for the ball – dodging, weaving, spell-binding, unleashing shots from every angle. It was exhilarating. He showed off all the tricks in his book. None of the guys defending could stop him. He ran back from scoring with the biggest grin.

On the sideline, his dad was frowning and Mr. Hammache was unreadable. Whatever. Kylian just did it all over again. He didn't pay attention when some of the other guys on his team called for a cross. He ignored it when some tall, bony kid whose name he'd forgotten scowled in his direction.

Two goals. He was beaming at the end of the first game.

"I want you to try out in defense in the second game," Mr. Hammache told him.

That's not going to happen, Kylian thought. *I'm a forward and we need someone who can attack and score. Let other kids do the heavy lifting in the back.*

During the second match, Kylian noticed his mom waving him back with that look she used when she wanted him to clean his room. But what was the point? Winning the ball and giving it to someone else to score was for losers.

"OK, Kylian," Mr. Hammache said at the end of the game. "Nice play. Sweet goals. You won us the game."

Kylian flashed his best smile.

"Thank you, Coach," he said

Hammache paused and gave him a stern look.

"But I asked you to defend. You didn't track back once. You didn't make one tackle. It left a big hole. They scored because of it. You know what that means?"

It means, I scored more, Kylian thought. He almost said it. But he held back. Good thing.

"It means I can't trust you. I can't trust you to play what's best for the team. Do you understand? I create a game plan. If you just go off and do whatever you want, it messes things up for the whole team. We're a team. Remember?"

Hammache didn't raise his voice, but no one had ever talked to Kylian like that before. Kylian couldn't believe it.

"Next game, you'll start on the bench. Have a nice day."

Benched? For an instant, Kylian stood rooted to the spot. He was shocked. Humiliated. He'd never been benched in his life. He had just scored all the goals and won the game for the team. *They can't bench me*, he thought. He opened his mouth, to express his thoughts, but Mr. Hammache had already gone.

He stormed across to Mom and Dad and told them what the coach had said to him. Mr. Hammache wasn't fair! He waved his arms around, but his parents didn't seem to care. They just shrugged.

"You do what the coach tells you to do," his mom said.

It was so annoying. The anger was building in his chest like a volcano.

For the whole first half of the third game, Kylian sat fuming. Part of him reluctantly accepted the coach's comments. If you didn't do your job for the team, you couldn't be picked. Yet, it didn't make him less angry. It was still humiliating.

That maybe it was his own fault – a fleeting thought – well, it just made things worse.

Besides, he was *best* at attacking. He watched his teammates playing. He was better than all of them.

Hammache's boys won a free kick just outside the box. Mr. Hammache signaled he wanted to make a substitution. He turned to Kylian.

"Tracksuit off, young man. You're going on. Right wing. But take this free kick first." It was like he was talking down to him. Like he was treating him like a little boy.

Kylian felt the boiling anger. But it was good to be on the pitch again. Where he belonged.

When he got the ball, he forced himself to calm down. He asked the referee where the spot was and placed it as meticulously as if it was a new poster of Zidane going up on his wall.

He looked up at the other team's wall, at the goal, at the keeper, then took a deep breath, struck the ball in the air, and watched.

Over the wall it flew, arcing like a frisbee.

It went into the top corner. The keeper just looked at it as if he was following a flying saucer.

Kylian leaped in the air and heard the cheers

The rest of the game was amazing. Playing was natural. Playing was feeling alive. But he had to remind himself that he wasn't playing alone. It was hard.

His mom, dad, and Uncle Pierre laughed all the way home.

"That guy has you pegged!" Uncle Pierre said. "You're great, but no one is bigger than the team."

"This is what you get when you get too big for your boots," Dad said.

Kylian sighed. He understood, but it was a lot harder to take than he thought.

The following week, he was surfing the net and found a YouTube film of the Gif-sur-Yvette tournament.

Only it wasn't the tournament – it was just him. A highlights reel.

The new Robinho! some guy in the comments said.

Oh wow! Kylian thought. He couldn't believe it.

"Mom," he screamed. "I want to show you something!"

CHAPTER EIGHT

You Can't Catch a Shark With a Fishing Rod!

Since the YouTube compilation, scouts from League One clubs had been a weekly sight at Bondy Under-Thirteen games. PSG. Bordeaux. Caen. Racing Club of Lens. He counted them in his head. He wasn't old enough to sign a full contract yet – but with Mom and Dad's permission, he could commit to a club so that when he was fifteen, he could start as an apprentice player.

He wore the Nike boots the people at Caen had sent him for his twelfth birthday. That was unreal too. Presents from recruiters. Especially since they were good boots. Supple, springy, with a giant sweet spot when you lined up a shot. Caen was the most serious of the clubs wooing him. They'd actually made an offer. Phoned it in. Dad thought the offer was too low. That was when he said his classic line. It made sense to Kylian.

"I must be missing something," Dad said. "You can't catch a shark with a fishing rod!"

Dad thought he was a shark! Kind of hard to sweeetspot a ball when you're a shark.

He wasn't supposed to know what Dad was talking about, but it wasn't rocket science. He was the shark, and they were trying to catch him with a fishing pole.

Mom and Dad did talk to him about the recruiters. "Don't make any promises," they'd told him. "We'll make a decision together, based on what's best for your future."

Fine by him. He just wanted to play in a top team.

But Caen's low offer wasn't good enough. His parents were confident that something better would come his way soon.

Kylian was deep in thought as he sat in the Bondy Under-Thirteen changing room waiting for the rest of the team when the door burst open. Théo, Joe, Jonathan, and the others clattered in. Mr. Fanfan – who was coaching them again – was close behind.

"You got here first again!" Théo exclaimed. "Straight from school, I bet."

Théo turned to Jonathan and Joe, giggling. "You'll never guess what he was wearing to school today!"

Kylian groaned.

"Platform shoes, flares like a pair of upturned buckets, and a shirt with orange swirls!"

Kylian threw his arms up in the air. "It was Mom's fault!"

"Looked like a clown," Théo went on.

"At least I'm still the best at football," Kylian countered.

"He made fun of Alain's hoodie yesterday," Théo said. "And somehow Fayza found out."

"No son of mine is going to act like a jerk," his mom had said to him.

God knew how she found out everything about him. Sometimes Kylian thought she had planted a hidden camera in his head.

"She really made you wear flares?" Joe exclaimed.

He nodded and hung his head in mock shame.

Mr. Fanfan grinned broadly. "Pay attention, Kylian. You're lucky you have a mom who won't let all this go to your head."

"Yes, sir." Kylian rolled his eyes.

When he grew up, he thanked her for being so tough on him. He guessed it kept his feet on the ground.

Even if he was a shark, he was still only twelve, and he had everything to look forward to.

After training, he asked Mr. Fanfan if they could talk.

"We are going up to Normandy for the Jean Pingeon Challenge," he began.

"It's a good arena," Fanfan agreed. He knew already, but he waited to see what Kylian had to say.

"We decided that Caen is the most serious about me," Kylian explained. "My parents thought it was best to see how the Caen coaches work with me, so I'm going to play with them in the tournament."

Fanfan gave him a level look. "And you agree?"

Kylian nodded.

"Well, I'm proud of you. You're growing up!"

Kylian nodded. "I-I wanted to ask you. You know my game. How should I play when I'm there?"

Fanfan smiled. "Just be yourself. But remember. The greatest players are creators. They see the others in the game, not only themselves. Show them you see the entire game. Don't think the only way to impress is to do everything yourself."

Kylian nodded. "Thank you, sir. That's good to know."

"Better, if you also remember to do it," Fanfan replied and flashed a grin. "And track back every once in a while!"

Ethan was on his best behavior when they drove through the miles of rolling hills, wheat fields, and orchards to Caen. When they stopped for a snack, Kylian liked the look of the cider and the long flat crusty bread, but he stuck with water.

The Jean Pingeon Challenge went by in a whirlwind.

He remembered racing downfield with the ball at his feet, threading past defenders as if they were cones.

He remembered working deftly into space and wishing with all his might for the ball.

He remembered a free kick that went spiraling over the opposite end of the wall from the goalie, leaving the guy open-mouthed with disbelief.

He remembered holding the ball up while his teammates found runs into the box and making a pinpoint cross.

He forgot to track back. Oh well.

They still made him Player of the Tournament.

CHAPTER NINE

Chelsea Calling

Dad handed Mom the letter. She scanned it, shrugged, and passed it back.

"How'd you like to go to London?" she asked Kylian.

He was drinking chocolate from a large glass and nibbling on a croissant stuffed with cheese. Ethan copied his every gesture. Kylian looked between his mom and dad, confused. "What's going on?"

Mom started reading the letter aloud.

Kylian listened intently.

"They want me to try out at Chelsea? In England?" he asked when she was done.

Mom nodded. "Like I said, London." She tapped the table-top and addressed his dad.

"What do you think, Wilfrid? Chelsea? We agreed it's between Caen, who are so keen, and Lens, where Mr. Hammache went. Will it help Kylian with his application to the Clairefontaine Academy? It's nice. It shows Kylian's got some worth. But what else?"

His dad was thinking.

"I think it's an extra option. Especially with what Jirès says about Lens."

His mom said, "I like Reda Hammache. He understands Kylian."

"I like him too," his dad replied. "But the Lens squad isn't doing great."

Kylian took no notice. He was happy scoring goals and ruling the roost with his friends in Bondy. Fifty goals so far this season. The way he saw it, the priority was to get his place in the Clairefontaine Academy where Jirès had gone. But Chelsea was a top club. And traveling to a foreign country would be exciting.

"Chelsea would be fun," Kylian said aloud. "I could meet Didier Drogba, maybe. And the English style of football is so different. I would learn."

"Drogba is not Zidane!" his mom said, smiling. "You are aware of that, right?"

Now it was Kylian's turn to smirk. "Yes, I am aware they are two completely different people. But..."

"But?" Dad asked.

"He is from Africa," Kylian replied.

Mom thought about it and nodded, then smiled up at Dad. "OK. We could make it a holiday. Let's do it, Wilfrid!"

Kylian thought that the England he saw through the window of the Eurostar train was pretty much like Normandy. And the outskirts of London were not so different from Paris – except for the river, which was wider than the Seine and full of container ships.

Stamford Bridge took his breath away. He knew the Parc des Princes, where PSG played, but this was so much more modern. And the trophy cabinet was immense and intimidating. FA Cup and Premier League trophies, all gleaming and golden in one place.

It took his breath away.

One day, he thought, *one day, I will bring trophies back to Paris. To Bondy.*

They spent a week at Chelsea's Cobham Training Centre. The other guys were mostly from England, though their families came from all over. Kylian had to listen hard to follow the coach's instructions. He realized Mom's sternness about learning English had been worth it. Soon enough, his skill and energy put him at the heart of everything.

The last day was a dream.

He ran out for the Chelsea Under-Twelves against Charlton – a local derby, like PSG going up against Bondy. They put him on the right wing, his favorite position. As soon as the ball left the center circle, he was on fire.

A neat one-two with the striker sent him on a trademark dribbling surge down his wing. The defense didn't back off, and Kylian dinked and yo-yoed the ball as if it was on elastic, leaving them floundering. He got to midway between the box and the by-line and spotted the striker again. His cross lasered onto the guy's head. One-Zero to the Blues.

Kylian the creator laid waste to the Charlton boys for the whole game. Chelsea scored seven in the end. Kylian's goal came from a free kick he won when the Charlton center-back got tired of Kylian's impossibly fast feet tricking him. The free kick was a beauty. He came barrelling up and shaped a spearing shot to the left of the wall. The keeper twitched. Kylian knew he would, and in an instant spun and delicately lobbed over the right end of the wall. The keeper kicked the ball back into the side-netting in disgust.

And that wasn't even the best part of the day.

Close to the end of the game, a towering kingly figure in a gray and black tracksuit appeared on the sideline. Kylian recognized him instantly and nearly lost the ball in his excitement.

Didier Drogba!

He sprinted over when the final whistle went. Drogba exchanged pleasantries with his dad in French.

"Ah! The wizard!" the great man boomed down at Kylian, reaching out his hand.

Kylian's smile was so wide he almost cracked his face. But he didn't lose his cool.

"Great to meet you," he said, returning the handshake firmly. "Your opening goal last night. It was the best."

"Yours wasn't bad either," Drogba quipped.

Kylian thought he would blow apart with pride.

When he got back to Bondy, he pinned the selfie he'd taken with Drogba on the wall, next to Zidane.

Ethan bounced in. "You want to go on PlayStation?"

"Sure."

As they dueled, Kylian looked back at the week. It had been so exciting, but he loved being with his own back home.

He wanted to play in France.

CHAPTER TEN

The Try-Out

The Clairefontaine try-out weekend was straight after coming back from Chelsea.

For once, there were butterflies in Kylian's stomach.

Mom drove, making a constant stream of chatter, but she didn't say anything about the try-out.

"Use your blinker!" she exploded at the driver ahead as they came to a junction.

Kylian grinned. She was always like this at the wheel. No one was as good a driver as her.

The Academy was a long white palace set in parklands. It looked like royalty still lived there.

Kylian trooped out of the car with a bag nearly as heavy as he was. Spare sneakers, shorts, shirts, tracksuits. PlayStation, shoes, polo shirt, and jeans for the evenings.

Jirès had already been a student there, so Fayza knew her way around.

The woman at reception checked Kylian's name on the PC and handed him a keycard and a joining pack.

"Through those doors, then keep going. Assemble in the briefing room at one p.m." She smiled. "Good luck."

Kylian smiled back.

His mom put her hands on his shoulders and squared him up. He was taller than her now. He only half heard her parting advice.

"Pay attention Kylian and just be yourself."

He smiled. She wasn't sure he'd heard her, but she sighed and kissed him on both cheeks. "See you Sunday."

"See you Sunday, Mom," he replied. Then he was alone.

The guys in the briefing room seemed pretty normal. About half were from the Paris outskirts like him, from the *banlieues*, the working-class suburbs of Paris, filled with African or Algerian families. There were a couple of skinny white guys. One spoke like he belonged on the radio, or was a politician. It didn't take long for introductions. Before long, the room was full of noise and banter.

"Attention!"

The voice boomed and echoed in the room. Everyone grew silent. That was when Kylian saw two men in immaculate tracksuits appear at the back of the room. Kylian squinted at their name badges: *Jacques Lafitte, Head of Development* and *Thierry de la Fontaine, Skills Director.*

The first briefing took ten minutes, then they were out on the training fields, doing drills.

It was the toughest couple of days of Kylian's life – harder than Gif-sur-Yvette, harder than Chelsea. It made sense. These were all the best youth players in France. Everyone could pass, cross, shoot, dribble, and tackle. For the first time, Kylian thought there might be someone here better than him.

The two instructors split them into four nine-a-side teams as well as doing drills; and kept changing the players' positions.

It was a real test.

Kylian set off on a run. The guy facing – he didn't know him – dared him to go past, so Kylian feinted and weaved, all part of his routine.

Except suddenly he no longer had the ball. The guy had anticipated his move and taken it away from him.

That was new.

For a second, Kylian froze. Then he caught sight of the instructors at pitch-side, iPads in hand, staring at him. Checking out his reactions.

He spun. The guy who'd dispossessed him started his own run, head up, looking for someone to pass to. Kylian chased him with a spurt of raw acceleration – but he wasn't fast enough. The ball was already on its way. He mumbled to himself.

This was a *real* test.

So he upped his game.

They finished the first day with a free kick drill. Kylian pulled it all out of the bag, five out of five firecrackers – dipping, swerving, rocketing, giving the keeper no chance.

But he was not the only one.

Over dinner, the guy who'd dispossessed him came over. "Wow, those free kicks," he said, shaking his fingers like they'd been burned.

The next day began with an academic interview, then it was back outside. Kylian was determined to go one up.

They did a dribbling drill against players, not cones. It was actually hard. Kylian had to battle. At the end of his last run, when he'd made it past every player, composed himself, and shot assuredly, he heaved a sigh and fist-pumped quietly.

He wished he could be sure that was a smile he'd seen on Mr. Lafitte's face.

"I lost the ball. So many times."

Kylian was sitting with Mr. Fanfan and the Bondy team.

"I'm desperate to go, but..." He threw his arms wide. "My mom and dad are going to Caen and Lens next week, to talk about my pre-contract, but I think it could be all over. If I don't get into Clairefontaine, they won't want me."

Théo, Jonathan, Metehan, and Joe looked at him like he was insane.

"Serious, bro! No call from Clairefontaine, no letter, nothing. I tell you. I didn't make it this year," Kylian insisted.

"Relax, it's been less than a week," Fanfan said. "They haven't even had their selection meeting yet." He put a hand on Kylian's shoulder. "You, my friend, will be fine."

Kylian scowled. Never had he felt any doubt. But this time was different. He wanted it so much, but the other kids were so good. He was anxious and worried.

He slunk back to his room when he got home and chucked his bag on the floor. Then he saw a piece of paper on his bed. His heart raced.

He opened it up. An email print-out.

Subject: Clairefontaine Academy application.

Oh, God.

Not till he'd gone through the text four times did he take it in.

He was invited to join the Academy! They had a place for him.

Why hadn't anybody said anything?

He exploded out of his room. They were all just outside. Dad winked.

"You knew..." Kylian said, feeling a smile coming on.

"And I guess you're always the last to know, son," Dad quipped.

Then everyone burst out laughing.

CHAPTER ELEVEN

Home and Away

The thumping and laughter in the dormitory was deafening.

Over the bed, off the walls, through the space between desk and sink, the tennis ball pinged and Kylian and his two roommates thundered.

There was just about enough space to dribble, to bounce the little green ball onto his instep and then spank it through someone's legs. But once you turned and tried tackling, it was like a dog fight.

They hurdled into each other, sprawling on the rug, making the tubular steel chair crash and ring with each impact.

The bottom half of the door was their goal, but none of the three boys really defended it. Tennis ball soccer was every man (or dog) for himself, a mad tangle of keeping the ball, threading it into impossible places until it hit the front of the door where it ricocheted the length of the room and back again.

Kylian, Jacques, and Dany weren't the only ones who filled their weekday evenings at Clairefontaine Academy with kickabouts, but Kylian liked to think they were the best.

Jacques caught the frayed ball with a cultured heave of his outside toes. It whirred out of the open window into the cool night air. Kylian winced, and all three waited in suspense. When no sound of crashing glass reached their ears, they fell down in shrieks of laughter.

"He breaks the net!"

"The Ultras go wild!"

"The World Cup belongs again to..."

"F-R-A-N-C-E!"

"We should get one of those really bouncy rubber balls," Dany said.

"No way! You smashed my desk light last time and got me in such trouble!" Kylian retorted.

"PlayStation?" That was Jacques.

"Let's go outside. Pitch One floodlights are on," Dany said.

"OK." Kylian said. "Get Ousman. We'll go two against two."

Kylian could never decide whether these night playtimes or the serious afternoon training sessions were the best part about going to Clairefontaine Academy. The training was ruthless. Always working on the weakest part of your game: the foot you didn't like, off-the-ball running, complicated technical practices, again and again. He had to admit it worked. His control was ten times better than even he had imagined possible seven months ago when the year began. Then there was all that stuff you had to *take time* about. But the best thing about the Academy was that it put him against guys whose brains worked nearly as fast as his, who weren't afraid and who didn't give up. It honed him.

The four were soon absorbed, not noticing the chill or the yellowish light of the floodlights. It was insanely fast. When Kylian had the ball, Ousman or Dany closed him down like lightning, dinking the way he did, blocking his options, forcing him wide. More than once, they darted in, poking the ball just as he shaped it, stepping across his line, getting their bodies in the way. Over the months he'd gotten better at shielding. He'd learned that he had to, but so had they. When he finally got away, it was exhilarating.

After an hour, they slumped by the goal, exhausted and giggling.

He loved Clairefontaine.

In the morning, he packed a bag ready for the weekend back in Bondy. That was all part of the routine. Weekday mornings – school. Afternoons – training. Then on Saturday and Sunday, back home. His mom picked him up. As they snaked out onto the *autoroute*, Kylian asked about the one thing that made him anxious.

"Have Caen sent a contract yet?"

Mom told him they were still waiting.

Kylian ground his teeth. At the end of last season, after Clairefontaine accepted him, they'd all agreed Caen was the best option for his apprentice years. The club had ambition, a family atmosphere, and was small enough that Kylian would get first-team experience quickly. He'd develop fast. Lens had been relegated.

But now, Caen was taking its time and wouldn't seal the deal. He wondered if he wasn't good enough?

He was angry and nervous. Most of the guys at Clairefontaine had contracts now, but only a couple with League One clubs. He knew he was at least as good as they were.

They drove straight to Bondy stadium. Théo, Metehan, Jonathan, and Joe were all there. They gave one another high-fives. It was great to play with them on Sundays.

Today was a cup game. They would make the quarter-finals if they won. Ousman, his mate from Clairefontaine, was on the other team.

Kylian and his friends pulled on their jerseys and tied their laces.

"It's a hat-trick day," Joe said. "I feel it in my toes."

Kylian grinned. "Watch out for Ousman," he said. "Intercepts like a ninja, but he likes it too much. You can pull him out of shape."

They touched hands in the middle of their huddle and ran out onto the pitch.

Kylian loved the competition of these home games. Loved being the engine of the team, winning not just for himself, but for the *banlieue*, the neighborhood. For Bondy. For home. He recognized the faces in the crowd. Avid, enthusiastic fans. Best of all were the roars of joy when he scored. It made him play better. These were his people.

Today was no exception. Almost from his first touch, Kylian drove the game. A little dink, a one-two with Metehan, and he was in space. Ousman tracked him. Kylian grinned to himself. Joe and Jonathan were both in good positions. He feinted a pass to Metehan – shaped, swung his leg. Then, as Ousman charged out of the line, he twisted the outside of his boot to take the ball and continue his own run. Ousman floundered. Kylian sent an instant low cross that Joe latched onto in a flash and volleyed home.

"You gave me every goal," Joe said, gripping Kylian's hand as they high-fived at the end of the match.

"You said it was a hat-trick day!" Kylian winked.

They laughed. He was happy.

CHAPTER TWELVE

Zidane!

"I told all the clubs it was you. You can't let him go!"

It was Fayza on the phone. Kylian sat in the living room, ears burning.

Laurent Glaize, the guy at Caen, was on the other end.

Mom slammed the receiver down and turned to him, her eyes a mixture of rage and sympathy.

"They can't afford me," Kylian said before she could open her mouth. "It's OK. It's been hard for them since they were relegated. I understand."

Fayza let out a sigh. She had no idea Kylian had followed Caen's fortunes so closely. Sometimes, her fourteen-year-old son showed a wisdom far beyond the rest of them combined.

"Everyone'll be fighting for you once it gets out." She smiled. "Did Dad tell you? We had an email from Manchester City..."

She trailed off when Kylian shook his head.

"My heart's in France, Mom."

She nodded, lips pursed. "We'll find something. What will you tell them at Clairefontaine?"

He was in his second year now. He shrugged. "The truth. The sooner the news gets out, the better."

He shouldered his bag. There were still a few weeks to go before the winter break. He was eager to get back to training. He could already see what would happen. He'd pout and throw up his hands when he told the story. *Baby-face, you cost too much!* It would be a blast.

When Fayza got back from taking him, Wilfrid beckoned her into the study and pointed at the computer screen.

"Take a look."

Fayza read the email. Her eyebrows shot to the top of her head and she huffed.

"It's near his birthday," Wilfried said. "It could be quite a present!"

Fayza laughed. "Do you remember when Hammache first spotted him? What he promised Pierre?"

"So he did!" Wilfrid giggled. "Who'd have thought it?"

The email was from Real Madrid, inviting Kylian to a week of training, meeting, and greeting. Zinedine Zidane, the legend, now manager of the Spanish super club, had signed it himself. The invitation was a great boost after the disappointment with Caen.

It turned out even better still. A month later, on the edge of his seat in the Bernabéu stadium, Kylian was in awe. The place was vast, nearly twice the size of Stamford Bridge or the Parc des Princes. Red and yellow smoke drifted high over the bright green of the pitch. The zarzuela brass band stationed behind the goal blared incessantly, like it was a carnival. Kylian revelled in the deafening noise of the crowd. It was bigger and more impressive than anything he had experienced so far.

Down on the field, Cristiano Ronaldo had the ball and was going up through the gears. It was so much more exciting than watching him on TV. He was like a giant. You sensed it in the crowd's reaction when he touched the ball. Sixty thousand people holding their breath as if they were all one person. Ronaldo's feet were incomprehensibly quick. He found himself in a scoring position and let fly. The keeper dove desperately, but the shot missed. The crowd exhaled. It was like the sea going out.

Kylian realized he'd risen to his feet and was cheering like everyone else. He sat down. The smile on his face lit his whole body, even his feet.

Training next day under Zinedine Zidane himself was no less brilliant. Like Ronaldo, Zidane felt bigger in real life. The eyes in his bald bullet head examined everything with an intensity that was almost blinding, though his smile and the welcome in his body were infectious. He paid attention to every detail. Kylian wasn't fazed by the man's scrutiny of his play. There was no pressure. He knew the Bernabéu wasn't for him just now. He could just enjoy himself.

Exuberantly, Kylian spun on the ball, deftly flicking it past the young Madrid lad who'd come to tackle him. It landed by Kylian's wrong foot, but the hours of drilling beneath the Clairefontaine trees paid off. He slid gracefully forward, the ball skimming obediently ahead like a dog chasing a stick. Then he saw the center-back making a beeline toward him.

His attention snapped back. The guy in goal had come forward, monitoring the player to Kylian's left, who shaped to receive a pass. Calmly, looking the center-back in the eye, Kylian lifted the ball in a sudden high arc. The center-back's feet stuck in the ground as it sailed over his head. The keeper saw the danger too late. He back-pedalled frantically, but it was no use. The ball dropped unerringly into the net before he could dive. Kylian gave a little leap and a fist-pump.

"So," Zidane was saying to Pierre, Fayza, and Wilfrid as Kylian came up at the end of the session. "We make sure it's a safe environment for our teenage players, as well as tailoring their opportunities. Kylian is a great talent. He'll train alongside the first team."

But Kylian wasn't listening. Over the other side of the pitch, just coming out of the development center, was the Real Madrid team. With Ronaldo!

Stay cool, Kylian told himself.

Then he was racing across the pitch.

"Baby-face, you are a fan-boy!" Théo teased.

"No way!" Kylian protested.

They crowded around his phone and the pictures of Kylian with his heroes. Ronaldo. Zizou.

"The V sign?" Joe mocked.

"To encourage him!" Kylian blustered. "They only drew their game. He needed a lift!"

"From a skinny baby-face who'd fall down if you flicked him?"

"Shut up, Metehan," Kylian pouted.

The boys laughed.

Wilfrid poked his head through the changing room door. "Finished?"

"Dad!" Kylian pouted again. He caught Théo's eye and sent him into another fit.

"Dad says pizza!" Wilfrid dead-panned. "And there's something we need to discuss."

"Uh-oh!" Kylian's friends chorused, their voices rising.

"All right guys, take it easy!" Kylian got up. "See you next weekend."

As they drove out onto the *autoroute*, Kylian eyed Dad. "So, what's up?"

"Nothing," Wilfrid replied. "Only... You remember Mr. Hammache? Used to be at Rennes? Then Lens? You liked him."

"Sure."

"He's scouting for Monaco now. And he's been on the phone. It's a long way from Paris though."

"They've just been promoted to League One," Kylian said, all ears now. He paused. "I'd still be able to come home?"

Wilfred grinned. Just like Kylian. Always one step ahead, on the field and off.

CHAPTER THIRTEEN

Rage

"To me!" Kylian's voice echoed futilely in the chilly, night-time ground. No one was passing to him, and he was angry.

It was pointless. His game was going nowhere. He should never have agreed.

Six months ago, Mr. Hammache and Mr. Camara had huddled over the coffee table at home in Bondy and everything had seemed easy. He'd signed the three-year apprentice contract, along with Mom and Dad. They all trusted Mr. Hammache.

The problem was, Mr. Hammache wasn't his coach at Monaco. Mr. Bruno Irles was. And Coach Irles didn't like him.

The assists he made, the chances he created, the goals he scored – they didn't count, only mistakes in the back third of the pitch.

Kylian didn't think he made *that* many.

Defence is not my game, he fumed to himself.

He was frustrated. Instead of turning out for the Monaco Under-Seventeens in the national league, where he belonged, he was playing with the amateurs. The same level as playing for Bondy. Only without his friends, and without the home crowd who appreciated every move he made.

It wasn't fair.

He screamed for the ball again, running into a perfect position, wide open down the right flank. *Just send me the ball,* he wanted to scream.

His teammate rolled a short pass, far too slow, and the ball was pounced upon.

Kylian stood where he was, roaring with frustration, watching the midfield back-pedal.

Stay put, his instincts told him. *Be there for the long ball. You'll get a one-on-one.*

From the sideline, his coach yelled at him, gesturing flamboyantly, angrily even. Kylian just glared.

The guy wants me to track back.

He flung his arms wide, pointing to the plenty of room he was in, but his coach shook his head and jerked his thumb in the direction of his own goal.

Kylian boiled over.

What was the point? The guy just couldn't *see!*

He gestured with his finger. Something Mom and Dad had taught him *never* to do. And he regretted it the second he did it.

"Don't. You. Ever. Do. That. Again."

Dad had his *I'm deadly serious face* on. "I realize Bruno doesn't get you, but you lost it, son. You did exactly the wrong thing."

Kylian hung his head. He knew it was stupid to lose his temper. But he also couldn't help thinking that biting back his anger had gotten him nowhere. He was back with the rest of the training side. Not so much game time, but at least the players knew what they were doing.

He couldn't help thinking that his mom would probably laugh it off and tell him to move on. Kylian was packing, getting ready to go on the team minibus for the Montaigne Cup in Nantes. He wasn't happy. His dad and he lived in a rented apartment in Monaco. His dad had taken a year off work to take care of his son. And he attended every training session.

He was still venting about his coach. His dad listened and said, "Bruno has a point when he says you aren't a star yet. And you need to play with the team. Not everyone is good as you are. So think how you could improve their game and make the team better."

"It's not easy," Kylian mumbled.

"Who said this was going to be easy?" Dad replied. "And guess what – it's going to become harder."

They did well in the cup. Kylian played well.

He was feeling fine when he saw his coach waving at him.

"You're looking beat, Kylian. One last effort. I'll bring you off in a couple of minutes."

That was it. Kylian's anger boiled and exploded. Before he could stop himself, he flung his arm and gave his coach the finger.

"Enough. On the bench. Now," his coach roared in anger, his face a picture of fury.

"NO!" Kylian yelled back.

"Now!"

He left the pitch deflated.

"Why can't I control myself?" Kylian admonished himself as the weeks drew on. "Why was I so stupid?" Mr. Bailaro, the Under-Nineteen coach was nearby and heard him talking to himself.

"Acceptance," Bailaro said.

Kylian could feel his face flush with embarrassment. He sighed. "I wish I knew what that was."

"You need to know what you can change and what you can't." He strolled away.

The evening sun cast long shadows over Monaco's La Turbie training grounds. Once again, Kylian had had an awesome individual training session – but ever since Nantes, that was all he had. Mr. Irles wouldn't speak to him, select him, or even have him train with the Under-Seventeens.

Dad said Mr. Hammache and Mr. Camara were trying to change his coach's mind about it, but Irles was adamant.

"Kylian?"

It was Mr. Bailaro again coming to his rescue. Kylian looked up, shading his eyes. Mr. Bailaro smiled and sat down.

"That's funny, I was just thinking about all this. I can't change it."

Bailaro grinned. "That's right," he said and put his arm around Kylian's shoulders. "Missing your team?"

"Totally. I'm so stupid."

"We all are," Bailaro said. "Now and then." He shrugged. "Teenagers are worse."

Kylian laughed. It was the first time he'd laughed in weeks. It felt good.

Mr. Bailaro sat back and looked him up and down. Kylian was so dejected and sad.

"Tell you what," he said. "Come and train with my lads tomorrow. Can't guarantee you a game, but let's see what we can make of you."

Kylian couldn't believe his ears. It was all he could do to stop the tears from coming into his eyes.

"I'll be there, Coach," he said. "Thank you."

CHAPTER FOURTEEN

On the Head!

Training with Mr. Bailaro was different from anything he had done before. Kylian had a lot to learn, and his new coach knew how to get things done without lighting his anger fuse.

It was September, a new season. Irles had gone on sabbatical for a coaching qualification, and Bailaro had the Under-Seventeens as well as the Under-Nineteens. Kylian was back with his team.

They'd just finished the afternoon session at La Turbie. It had ended with a five-a-side, and Kylian had failed to get on the end of a couple of crosses. After training, they all gathered and Mr. Bailaro turned to him.

He didn't speak, just raised his eyebrows with an inquisitive look and pointed to Kylian's forehead. Kylian's mouth twitched, trying not to laugh. Mr. Bailaro looked puzzled, then took Kylian's head in his hands and peered at it, frowning. He looked back at the rest of the huddle.

"Well, it looks like young Mbappe has a brain like the rest of us. What do you think?"

Kylian's eyes turned to the sky, but he was smiling.

It was hard to explain. His feet always felt like they had brains of their own. They were like magnets, drawn to the ball, and they could make it move like they had it on remote control. His head just felt like it was there to look and see. If a cross came in, his instinct was to jump and bring his feet into play, not take the ball on his forehead – where it felt like a plate of jelly.

"Practice!" Bailaro said. "Tonight, in the game, I want to see you take a header. Two. Three. Just do it."

Kylian could head the ball fine if it was a drill, as sharply as anyone. He sighed. Mr. Bailaro was right of course. He squared his shoulders.

"OK, sir."

The game was against Lyon. In the first half, Kylian carved out a couple of chances for the team, but no shots came his way. In the half-time huddle, Mr. Bailaro reminded everyone.

"Kylian, I need you to offer yourself in the box. Get some crosses to him," he urged the other guys.

Ten minutes in, it happened. Monaco swept down the left flank and Kylian found space on the edge of the area. The ball sailed toward him. He charged forward and leaped, but the timing was wrong. The ball scuffed the corner of his head and ballooned wide. Kylian grimaced. On the sideline, Mr. Bailaro clapped with joy.

It was the same five minutes later. The whole action felt forced. Kylian used all his energy.

Nothing else came until stoppage time. Monaco won a free kick on the left wing. Bailaro waved Kylian into the area. Kylian's adrenaline surged as the ball came in.

It was shoulder-high and fast. For an instant, Kylian froze, then something clicked. There was no way he could volley, no time to chest the ball down. But if he hit the ground hard, it would hurt. So what?

His body was already airborne.

Everything happened in slow-motion. He saw the ball zeroing in. His head bent slightly back. It snapped forward, sharp, just as the ball met his own trajectory.

Bang!

Right on the sweet spot.

It lasered down, headed just inside the post.

Still in the air, Kylian felt a roar of triumph beginning inside him.

Then, to his horror, there were the keeper's fingertips, brushing the ball aside – just enough to deflect the ball onto the post. It bounded out of play.

Kylian plowed into the ground. The whistle went. He slapped the turf, wild with frustration. In his own mind, he had failed.

"Great Kylian! Great! You got the feel of it! Fantastic!" Mr. Bailaro pounded his back over and over as they came off the pitch. Kylian's face was scraped red.

"But I missed," he said frustrated.

Bailaro grinned. "You're missing the point."

"What?" Kylian was confused.

Bailaro put his hand on Kylian's shoulder. Kylian couldn't figure it out.

"You're happy?"

"More than happy," the coach said. "In fact, I'm moving you up. I'm putting you in my squad next week."

Kylian let out a breath. He had missed. Everyone misses. But there are great misses. The ones that show how good you are.

CHAPTER FIFTEEN

Making Progress

Kylian sat in the classroom, anxious. Distracted. There was still an hour and a half of school left before he could run out onto the La Turbie pitch and do what he was born to do. He stifled a sigh and looked down at the practice exam paper.

Kylian thought back over the year since Mr. Bailaro had put him in the Under-Nineteens, the two years since leaving Bondy.

He remembered his first Under-Nineteen goal in a competition. They'd flown to Corsica under the threat of a thunderstorm. He'd come off the bench. He remembered the feeling of vindication when he saw the ball in the back of the net and his new teammates all gathered around, celebrating.

A few weeks later, he'd run out against Zenit St. Petersburg, the Russian side, in the European Youth League. Monaco lost, but his late cross provided their only goal.

Then the football had gone mad. Game after game with the Under-Nineteen team. Up an age grade, like so many times before. Scoring. Entertaining.

It was because he never let go of what he knew about his own game. What he could see in his mind's eye when he was on the field. Even when Irles bawled him out. Even though they still hadn't called him back to the national youth squad.

He got results. He was proud of himself. Not long ago, he'd thought it was the end of the world. *Guess I was wrong*, he thought and smiled to himself.

Can we justify our beliefs? was the question he had to answer.

Yes. He could answer that. He started to write.

When the bell rang, there were two closely written sides of the paper. A testament.

Out on the training ground, they ran through the normal drills, then Mr. Bailaro gathered them in a huddle and started talking about their evening match against A.C. Ajaccio. It reminded Kylian of being in the Bondy changing rooms when he was little. He listened just like then, only with the buzz of knowing he would go out on the pitch and play.

"Sir." He put up his hand. "What do we know about their defensive system?"

Mr. Bailaro smiled. "Good question. They were well drilled last time. Tight back four. And as it's the same names on the team sheet tonight, we can assume they'll stick with that formation. We need to pull them out of shape. They hang off. So, Kylian, draw your marker wide and make space. Use your pace. Your dribbling too. The more confusion, the more gaps."

Kylian felt a rush of adrenaline. He had just been given a license to roam.

It was a home game, so they stayed at La Turbie until match time. Kylian was in the starting line-up.

When he ran on, the pitch was floodlit, sending star-shaped shadows from his feet. Dad and Uncle Pierre were in the stands. Théo and Mr. Fanfan were there too, visiting for the weekend.

As soon as they kicked off, Monaco pressed upfield. They played a canny passing game, daring and fast, helping one another out with runs, one-twos, and switches of play from wing to wing.

From the stands, the Mbappes and their friends cheered every surge along with the couple of hundred other spectators. Someone got out a trumpet and sent a bullfight fanfare into the night sky. "Ole!" the crowd replied.

From his vantage on the right, Kylian felt good, but after half an hour Monaco were still goalless. Once, Ajaccio broke the stranglehold, prompting a fingertip save. Kylian couldn't help seeing it had been the game's best chance so far.

He made himself available. The ball came to his feet. Within seconds, he'd burned his marker and the left-back who came across to cover. His path to the corner flag was unopposed – but that wouldn't do. He could see what would happen. Ajaccio's defense would close before he could cross. He had to go alone.

He swerved as if to go to the extreme right, drawing the center-back, then like lightning transferred his weight. The ball sang on the turf. He skipped the Ajaccio man's desperate foot. He reached the area. The keeper charged.

Kylian didn't miss a beat.

The same feint as before squared the goalie the wrong way. He tapped the ball past with his left foot and, as the Ajaccio cover thundered behind him, he lasered a shot into the middle of the goal.

One-zero.

He spun, eyes shining and determined, his celebration modest, and jogged upfield.

There was more to do.

His second came ten minutes into the second half. A one-two with Irvan took him down the middle. Ajaccio's back four lined up like a wall, but there was just the hint of an angle. On the edge of the area, he let fly. It shaved the center-back's ear and burned past the keeper's full-length dive.

Two-zero. Another modest celebration.

In the last minute, Ajaccio came away on the break, desperate for a consolation goal. Kylian raced off his wing, caught the attacker, and put in a perfect tackle from behind, collecting the ball and punting it into touch.

"Your boy's changed," Fanfan said, turning to Wilfrid as the players trooped off. "So calm, so mature on the pitch."

In the dressing room, Bailaro gave Kylian a thumbs-up. Kylian smiled. He felt solid. His feet were on the ground. He was where he wanted to be. Where he should be.

CHAPTER SIXTEEN

"Our Youngest Ever"

Kylian skipped off the Monaco youth team minibus after the drive back from La Turbie on a sunny September day. A breeze blew off the harbor, brushing the precincts of the Prince Louis II stadium with a slight chill. He was in good spirits as he strode through the arches inside and turned right into the corridor that led to his room.

The start of another season in Mr. Bailaro's Under-Nineteen squad. He'd already gotten on the score sheet. As he had for Monaco's senior reserves, in the French fourth division. Life was great.

"Mbappe!"

The voice was familiar, though he couldn't place the woman's name – one of the athletic, tanned administrators who worked in Leonardo Jardim's office.

"The boss wants you." The woman glanced at her watch. "In ten. You got the text?"

Text? Uh-oh.

His phone was out of juice.

"I must have got it, but I can't check right now. Battery died on my phone."

The woman looked at him coolly, hands on hips. "His office. Don't be late!"

He grinned, but his heart was pounding fast. What could Jardim want? It couldn't be about his contract.

For discussions like that, they went straight to Dad. Was Bruno Irles back to make his life a pain?

In his room with its view out to the yachts lining the harbor, Kylian brushed his hair and pulled on a fresh Monaco tracksuit. He was rapping Jardim's door bang on time.

"Kylian!" Mr. Jardim reached across his desk.

"Sir!" Kylian took the manager's hand firmly.

"Enjoying things now?" Mr. Jardim said, his eyes intent and the corners of his mouth crinkling. It wasn't really a question, so Kylian just nodded.

"No more misunderstandings with the coaches!"

Kylian felt himself flush with embarrassment and nodded again.

"Good!" Mr. Jardim's face was unreadable. "You like a challenge, eh? Respond well?"

"Yes, sir. I hope so."

Mr. Jardim harrumphed, his face turning downcast. "You saw our injury list."

Kylian frowned. The senior squad was in trouble. Mistakes. Call-ups. It was everyday gossip.

"Maybe you watch the chat rooms too, eh? You know who they're saying should fill the gap up front?"

Kylian shifted. Some of the fans were saying *he* should be drafted in. It would be a dream come true.

"You're a good kid." Mr. Jardim laughed. He leaned back in his seat. "What would you think if I told you, for once, the fans are onto something?"

Kylian blinked.

Mr. Jardim smiled. "I'm putting you on the senior squad. We have a session under lights tonight. Your kit is in the changing room. Number 29."

Kylian's mouth worked, but no words came out. Mr. Jardim stood up and slapped him on the shoulder.

"Cat got your tongue lad? Go on. Grab some pasta. See you in an hour."

Kylian just about managed to stammer his thanks. He went to the stadium cafeteria in a daze and only ate anything because Mr. Jardim had told him to.

When he walked into the senior squad room, it was empty. He looked around at the neatly hung kits, red and white, under their shining brass pegs and name-plates with the numbers and names of each squad member. Instinctively, he looked for number twelve. That would have been Thierry Henry's in the days when the French genius was learning his craft in the very same school. Some fans compared Kylian to Henry. Kylian thought that was exaggerated, even if it did give him a thrill. The thought brought a new feeling. He had to work hard to make the fans' dreams come true.

He went up to the shirt and fingered it, then looked around again for his own name. It was in the corner, just the number.

He sat down, glancing around. Fabinho, Carvalho, Bernardo Silva, and the captain and fellow Frenchman, Jeremy Toulalan. Names to savor. Men he would learn from.

The door opened. Three men walked in. Kylian took in their faces and silently rattled off their names from memory: Guido Carrillo, Ivan Cavaleiro, and Tiémoué Bakayoko, two fellow forwards and a midfielder. Bakayoko stopped and looked at Kylian inquiringly.

"Kylian Mbappe Lottin," Kylian said immediately, standing up and offering his hand.

"Tiémoué Bakayoko," the French international replied. "Who are you playing with now?"

Kylian smiled, his face lighting up. "I'm in the Academy here."

Bakayoko took a step back and surveyed Kylian from head to foot. "How come I've never seen you around?"

"I'm sixteen, sir," Kylian said. "I was only permanently moved up to Mr. Bailaro's guys this year. I've played in the reserves a couple of times."

"Sixteen!" Cavaleiro exclaimed. "What's your position?"

"Right-wing forward."

Cavaleiro smiled and stuck out a hand. "Welcome to the pros, kid!"

Soon, the whole squad filed in. Mr Jardim introduced Kylian. Some of the team nodded, recognizing the name. Then they went out on the pitch. It was Kylian's first run-out at Monaco's main stadium. He savored the echo around the empty stands. This was a Ligue One ground, and Kylian was kicking a ball on it in earnest. His chest swelled and his heart pumped. No way was he going down from here.

A week later, he was running out in the last minutes against Caen, making his debut.

Mom, Dad, Ethan, and Uncle Pierre were wrapped up in the crowd at the Louis II stadium. Monaco were already two-one in the lead. Kylian went on ten minutes from the end. The spectators yelled and bounced around in the stands, cheering for him. As injury time ticked onward, Helder Costa picked the ball up on the halfway line. Kylian took off down his wing, and the Portuguese man found him. Two touches, then Kylian sent the ball back to Costa. The return pass came to him on the edge of the area.

Kylian didn't hesitate.

Without breaking stride, he shot with his wrong foot, sending Matthieu Dreyer in the opposite direction to the ball.

Goal!

In the changing room, Toulalan called the squad to attention, his arm draped around Kylian's shoulders.

"Gentlemen, today a great player was born. For a long time, every record here belonged to Thierry Henry, but not anymore. Kylian Mbappe Lottin just became our youngest ever goal-scorer. And as of two months ago, he became the youngest to play for us in Ligue One!"

Everyone cheered and whooped.

"Not only that," Mr. Jardim added, waving his phone in the air. "I have an announcement. Kylian Mbappe has just been added to France's Under-Nineteen team. Ludovic Batelli just called me."

For a moment, Kylian just stood there. All his goals and progress at Monaco had meant nothing to the Under-Seventeen international squad! Now, he was about to join the Under-Ninteen squad! He looked over at Mom and Dad. Both had tears in their eyes.

Suddenly, nothing could contain his joy. He started leaping all over the place, and everyone jumped with him.

His face was covered with a huge, beautiful smile.

CHAPTER SEVENTEEN

Two Cups and a Coffee

"*How* did he get your name wrong?" Fayza shot Kylian a glance from the wheel of their car. She was driving him to the center of Paris for a team celebration. The wide suburban road gave way to the crowded but neat buildings of inner Paris. "He'll remember you now, son!"

Kylian grinned.

They'd beaten Lens three-one in the final of the Gambardella Cup, France's top youth tournament. On the grass of the Stade de France – the country's national pitch. It was his first trophy. What a place to triumph!

"The look on that guy's face when you corrected him!" She was mad about the TV reporter who interviewed him after the game. Kylian had flashed his most engaging smile when the reporter thrust a massive microphone in his face and called him some completely random name.

Thank God Kylian had imagined doing these interviews for years. He hadn't missed a beat.

Now, Kylian wondered idly if the man's mistake was because Kylian was a young black kid from the *banlieues*. It wasn't that long ago that Bondy had been famous for riots. But at no time in his training, wherever he was, had Kylian felt treated differently because of the color of his skin. Anyway, the presenter's cheeks had gone beet red under his TV make-up when Kylian corrected him.

"You won the cup on your own!" Fayza was overflowing with enthusiasm. "The way you took the midfield on for that first goal. Made the defender look you right in the eye. The no-look pass. Eye of a needle, my boy. Just like Bondy Juniors." She sniffed. "Oh, for goodness sake! I think I'm going to cry!"

"It was the team, Mom! It was all of us."

True, he'd buried two chances himself, as well as giving Irvin Cardona that initial assist. But it was still *everyone's* cup. Surely Mom knew that, being an athlete herself. When he'd scored that goal in League One, it was special. This was something else. Winning with teammates, with friends – it meant so much more.

He'd told the interviewer exactly that in the post-match session.

He entered the restaurant. The team table spotted him instantly and cheered as if to raise the dead. Irvin sprang out of his chair and slammed his open hand high into Kylian's.

"Yo, main man!" He leaned into Kylian's ear. "Thanks for the goal, bro!"

Kylian laughed and let himself get swallowed by the group. It was all football talk. It was what he loved best.

He felt great. And he wanted it to last forever.

First the Gambardella Cup, now the U19 Euros. Semi-final day.

Kylian got ready, eyes glowing, smile alive, on a typical July day for Germany, the tournament's venue this time. Sunlight belted across a turf that was only green because the ground's staff watered it day and night. On the other side of the halfway line, Portugal's lads stood firm, some looking as if they wanted to be sick, others as pumped and ready as Kylian.

The Portuguese youngsters had the discipline and craft of their greatest senior team. France had hardly seen the ball when – in the third minute of the game – Pedro Pacheco ran through France's back four and gave Portugal the lead.

Then Kylian got hold of the ball. A ragged shout of "Allez les Bleus – Allez Kylian" ("Go on you Blues – Go on Kylian") sounded from the Mbappe family stationed at the center of the band of French supporters.

Kylian responded – if the sun was hot, it was nothing to what he would put on the Portuguese defence! His burst of pace felt like a barrier going down. The wind on his face was like a storm, even though the air was still. Somehow, as the Kylian-tornado blasted down the left wing, Ludovic Blas, France's center forward, kept abreast in the middle. Kylian's cross arrived with the sweet ping of a tennis ball, and Blas met it perfectly.

A tie.

They double and triple-teamed Kylian after that.

It didn't faze him.

He ran, teasing them, knowing that in the end, in the blazing sun, they'd give up. He'd outlast them.

Midway through the second half, he broke through again and scored himself. A dozen minutes later, he added a second.

France had made it to the final against Italy.

In the dressing room two days later, before they took the field, listening to manager Ludovic Batelli's team talk, he felt himself slipping into the zone again.

"For France," he bellowed as they ran onto the pitch.

Kylian was dancing through the game. Italy had no answer other than to block and put men on him. Kylian didn't mind. It gave the rest of his teammates a lot of space.

Four-zero. A thrashing.

In the week between the end of the Euros and pre-season back at Monaco, Ethan gave him no peace.

"Show me the medal again! I want to wear it!"

Kylian couldn't deny him. When the winner's medal went around his neck, Ethan's eyes shone brighter than the gold itself. Kylian hugged his brother and laughed.

The night before going down to Monaco, Uncle Pierre knocked on the door of his room. Kylian's suitcase was open, and t-shirts, jeans, and socks were scattered all over the floor. Kylian sat with his FIFA PlayStation, mp3 earplugs in his ears, swaying.

"Kylian!" Uncle Pierre raised his voice.

"Uncle Pierre! Sorry!" Kylian unplugged his ears and stood up. He'd made a big deal about packing his own stuff. Now he'd been caught just taking a little break.

"No, no, don't be silly," Uncle Pierre waved him down. "I just wanted to give you this. Take it. It's not properly wrapped."

Kylian looked inside the bag and grinned.

"Highland Coffee Beans from Cameroon, with a grinder," Uncle Pierre explained. "I can't stand the stuff you keep in your room at the Louis II. Now at least I won't choke."

Kylian embraced him. "So, I'm a real man now," he joked. "I deserve my own grinder. I'll make coffee so strong you can stand the spoon up in it."

Uncle Pierre guffawed loudly and slapped Kylian's back.

"You are a man." He gazed at the unholy mess all over Kylian's floor. "Or becoming one..." He smiled. "This is going to be a big year for you. I feel it. Don't forget where you come from."

"Oh, don't worry. I'm Bondy forever," Kylian said.

Uncle Pierre nodded.

"And now you have the coffee to prove it!"

CHAPTER EIGHTEEN

An Explosion

Kylian couldn't help but keep thinking about what Uncle Pierre had said.

It had been nearly two months since the Euros. He'd come back to Monaco jumping for joy. Then, BAM. In the first pre-season clash he'd gone for a header – and had no memory of what happened next. He had been knocked out cold.

Everyone said he and Christophe Kerbrat had collided like two hammers, sending them both to the deck, unconscious. Kylian only remembered waking up on the wet grass and immediately wanting to get back to play. Instead, they whisked him to the hospital.

But the next day – and for a whole week – he'd woken up feeling like his body was a sack of potatoes and his head was in a fog. He never wanted to feel like that again.

When he was back, he saw something strange in Leonardo Jardim's eyes. Something was different.

The manager was distant.

Just that morning, they'd announced the squad going to White Hart Lane in London, for the Champions League qualifier against Tottenham.

Jardim hadn't picked him.

This'll be a big year for you. Those were his words, yet here he was, out of the roster.

He went out of the dressing room after the squad was read out, deflated. Later, he walked blindly along the harbor-front, losing track of time. He was hurt.

He never really understood just how much success meant to him. How much it meant to make his family truly proud of him. How desperate he was to go on to bigger and better things. After the injury, it was what kept him going.

Now, he only felt bewildered.

That was when there was a knock at the door. Voices. Mom, Dad, Uncle Pierre. They came in. They looked angry.

"I'm sorry," he began, "I just needed to..."

"My son," Fayza interrupted, resting her hand on his shoulder. "You have nothing to apologize for."

"Jardim..." Dad could hardly get the words out. His hands were balled tightly.

Uncle Pierre began to pace. "When we signed you up with Monaco, it was because they were supposed to nurture you. We had that problem with Bruno Irles, but it looked like you had finally found two men who knew your worth. Then this!"

Kylian followed his uncle with his eyes. He'd never seen him so incensed.

"What's going on?"

"Your father's right," Mom said. "It's like they're blind."

Dad's mouth was set in a tight line.

"You should be on that plane with them to London," Uncle Pierre went on. "We tried to get a meeting with Jardim, but his assistant wouldn't even look at us."

"It's supposed to be a big year," Kylian blurted out. In that instant, he wished he could shove the words back in his mouth. They were a child's words. He thought about what he could change and what he couldn't, remembering.

"That's exactly right," Uncle Pierre said. "In a fair world." He looked around and finally landed back on Kylian. "You know, Barca is interested. Manchester City even made an offer. We'll move on."

Kylian got a sinking feeling. He took a deep breath.

"I just have to carry on," he said. "They know who I am."

He could see Dad heaving a breath. Then Dad nodded and let his fists uncurl. "You're right, son."

He sat next to Kylian's mom.

"We'll be right behind you."

They embraced.

At last, Kylian let himself sob.

Kylian's resolution was easier said than done. He got back into the squad, but as autumn went on, he sat on the bench match after match, going on for only a few minutes here, a few there. Still, he played like a demon in training and didn't complain.

One night, in October, at the final whistle of a game against Toulouse when he'd not played at all, Jardim turned to him.

"We need you to strengthen the reserves tomorrow," the manager said, his voice firm. "It's a game we have to win."

Kylian's first thought gave him a bitter taste in his mouth, but then he caught himself and realized the full meaning of what Jardim was saying. More than that, what Jardim was going through. And despite everything, Jardim trusted him to make a difference.

"I'll make sure it happens," he said.

The next evening, as he ran out onto a windy pitch, he felt unleashed. He was in the game from the moment of kick-off. Flicks, dummies, dribbles, they were all there. One run ended with a firm side-foot into the back of the net. The second finish was a screaming short-range volley off a cross that didn't quite go where it was meant to.

The next day, Jardim congratulated him with the glow of a man who saw something he could build on. Kylian built no hopes up, but when Friday came, his name was on the League One starting sheet for the first time in the season.

He sat savoring it with his eyes closed – a heave of relief, then a rod of burning determination.

He was back.

CHAPTER NINETEEN

Rugrat

"Rugrat! Welcome to the Thunderdome!"

Benjamin Mendy, obviously. It had been the first thing Kylian heard the French defender say when he walked into the changing room for pre-season – the name of some cartoon babies on TV who were always saving the world. Mendy thought it was the best nickname. So did Kylian.

Since the concussion, no one had used it.

Mendy gave him a nudge. "Gonna save the team, Rugrat?"

Kylian held Mendy's gaze just a fraction before saying, very distinguished-like, "I'll do my best". They shared a laugh.

A smile the size of the Champs-Élysées spread over Bayakoko's face. Everyone knew just how much Kylian wanted to make his mark and how hard waiting had been.

"You're not alone," he said.

Falcao, the team's captain who was playing alongside Kylian up front, came and shook his hand warmly.

"Take it easy, Rugrat. You're gonna have lots of chances."

Kylian nodded, holding the captain's eye. They wanted to make sure he didn't tense up. Good for them.

That was how a senior pro should behave. *His* job was to show them he was calm. That he could do a job. He didn't feel nervous – just buzzing and alert.

"Show me what you're made of," Jardim whispered as they ran out onto the pitch. The manager smiled as if he too had the chance of a lifetime.

Kylian needed no second invitation.

·They were playing Montpellier, a seasoned mid-table team that reminded Kylian of Bondy.

Nine minutes in, the Montpellier member 10, Ryad Boudebouz, put one past Subasic in goal. The Monaco crowd went silent.

Kylian knew what he had to do.

He set off, his long legs taking him downfield like giant springs as the ball sped in front of him. A body dummy sent the first midfielder to reach him sprawling. Bernardo Silva headed for the far post. Kylian rocketed the cross.

Inches from Silva's head.

The Monaco end went crazy, anyway.

Soon, Kylian himself plugged in, volleying like a cannon-shot toward the right corner of the net. Geoffrey Jourdren, in goal, got a fingertip to push it wide.

Kylian's third surge was too much. It was obvious he was going to score. The only thing that could stop him was a crude shove. Monaco's captain, Falcao, slotted the penalty home.

It was just the beginning.

Four minutes into the second half, Kylian darted past his marker into the area. The cross came high. In Kylian's mind, he heard Mr. Bailaro's urging from what seemed a lifetime ago, though it was only a year.

Get it on your head boy. You're not exactly short! Bailaro had a way with words.

So Kylian soared.

Time slowed.

It was like the stars conspiring to come together. Head and shoulders higher than the Montpellier full-back, Kylian and the ball met.

Kylian's neck snapped.

The back of the net bloomed.

He wanted more. Moments later, he sent a pitch-perfect cross onto Valère Germain's head; and another for Thomas Lemar.

It wound up six-two. The team mobbed him in the changing room. Standing next to Leonardo Jardim for the post-match interview, Kylian nodded as his manager talked about how pleased he was, how Monaco was the right environment for him.

"I'm a competitor. It's frustrating when I can't play, but I'm learning all the time," Kylian said shyly.

"Rugrat, you've got the gift," Mendy said when they went back to the dressing room. "You could charm the legs off a donkey."

Kylian brayed like a donkey. Mendy slapped his back. They all laughed.

When he got out of the changing room, Uncle Pierre was waiting for him.

"That showed them! All is right with the world again!"

Kylian shook his head.

"It was just one match. I'm still part of a rotation and I truly think it's good for me, Uncle."

"I think you need another cup of coffee to plug that hole in your head!" his uncle said with a chuckle.

Kylian was right. He got more game time, but Jardim wasn't about to burn him out. He kept the youngster hungry. Kylian understood exactly what he was doing and set out to force his way up the pecking order.

"Today I'm going to send a message," he said.

It was December 14. He was in the starting line-up. A cup game against Rennais Town.

"Hey Rugrat, what message do you have for them today?"

"You don't want to know!" They both chuckled.

It was drizzling, but not cold, in the Stade Louis II. Not a full house, but that didn't matter once the Kylian show started.

No one could stop him. He burned up the left wing, cutting inside for once, spotting the Rennais keeper out of position. The finish was a thing of precision. Not a hammer blow, not a fancy trick, just perfect placing and perfect pace that left the keeper unable to move.

Then he was pouncing on a deflected shot from Nabil Dirar, steering it into the net before the defense could clear.

At last, he got the hat-trick. His first in a Monaco shirt. Professional, again, taking Moutinho's pass and smacking it home with his left foot.

"Hey, Ben," he said, as the team celebrated. He flashed three fingers. "Can you count?" Then he laughed like a jackal.

"OK. Rugrat. I owe ya. Three pizzas."

They smashed hands together.

CHAPTER TWENTY
Ambassador Kylian

Kylian relaxed in the buzz of the changing room. Monaco were playing Manchester City in the second leg of the Champions League round of sixteen. He was a starter, just as in the first leg in Manchester. Monaco had lost five-three, even though Kylian had woven all kinds of devilry. The press in England went crazy. Kylian ignored it. All that mattered was getting Monaco through to the quarter-finals.

As they lined up, he radiated intent.

Mendy grinned. "Rugrat, how do you like the Champions League?"

"I own it," Kylian replied, his eyes sizzling.

He was joking. The Manchester leg had been his first Champions League start. But he had to admit, it did feel different from League One. This was the adventure he had been waiting for.

Mendy shrugged expressively. "Well, we ain't got anything to lose, that's for sure. See you in Paradise."

It turned out to be a great game. Things had hardly started when Bernardo Silva fired in a low fast cross. Kylian hit it square, and the net bulked.

On the half-hour, he pounced again, poaching a wayward pass as Manchester City pressed dangerously forward. A spurt of fire from his legs bypassed the Sky

Blues midfield: the counter-attack was on. Fabinho slammed that one home.

In the end, Monaco had the victory, three goals to one. They'd done it. The next stop would be against Borussia Dortmund in April.

The next day, as they sat down after training, Kylian saw there was a missed call and message on his phone. He glanced at the number and handed it to Mendy.

"I don't know the number," he said. "You reply."

Mendy took the handset, grinning wickedly. Then his eyes widened. "Rugrat, you'd better listen to this one yourself."

He put the phone on speaker. "Kylian, it's Didier Deschamps. Give me a call."

Deschamps? The France national squad manager?

"It can't be real," Kylian said instantly. Mendy shook his head and pressed recall. Before Kylian could get the handset back, he heard a voice.

"Deschamps here."

Kylian's hands shook as he spoke. "Sir? Kylian Mbappe. I got your call?"

"Kylian, fantastic. I wanted you to hear it from me directly. I want you on the squad for the next two internationals."

Kylian looked at Mendy in disbelief. "Can life get any better?"

Mendy grinned. "Oh, it can get a lot better!"

"That's it, Bro! I won!"

Ethan caromed across the floor of the family's new Cap d'Ail apartment, knees on the floor, arms crossing his chest like a saint.

Kylian sat on the sofa, nodding his head in disbelief. It wasn't possible. His kid brother had just beaten him badly at FIFA PlayStation. It couldn't be, this never happened. Even if it was nine in the morning and he was about to set off on the team bus for the Champions League quarter-final first leg in Borussia Dortmund, this just wasn't right.

Ethan zoomed across the floor again, same posture, the mane of his shoulder-length dreadlocks brimming.

"Hey, brother," he said, as he whizzed past for a third time. "This is how you should celebrate your goals!"

Kylian raised an eyebrow and just sat there, watching his brother zip to and fro.

"You know what, Ethan? I just might."

Ethan stopped, his eyes the size of dinner plates. "Really?!"

"Yeah," Kylian replied.

"That would be so cool!"

Kylian grinned and made himself a little promise. "Watch my games and see."

"Every time they let me. Cross my heart."

From down the hall, Fayza bellowed that it was time to go. Kylian stood up. "I gotta catch the team bus now," he said and stuck out his hand. "Do we have a deal?"

Ethan grabbed his brother's hand and reeled him in and hugged him. "We have a deal."

Kylian strode out of the apartment, training bag over his shoulder. Fayza held the door of the car open.

"Ethan looks up to you," she said as they set off.

"I know, and I want to be a good role model for him," Kylian replied.

When they got to the Louis II stadium, everyone was looking pale.

"Hey, Rugrat," Mendy greeted him. "Did you hear? The Borussia team bus got bombed, but they're fine."

For a moment, Kylian's mind went blank. Then he scrambled for his phone.

It was all over social media.

Without a second thought, he tweeted Ousmane Dembele, a Bondy friend who was in the Borussia squad now.

Ousmane, you OK? Thoughts with all of you!

He didn't expect an answer, but he hoped his friend got it.

"Is the game still on?" he asked after the text went.

"Tomorrow," Mendy nodded.

"We should show our solidarity."

"Good idea."

The next night, in front of the Borussia "yellow wall," the atmosphere was emotional. Kylian ran around all the Borussia players, shaking hands, and embracing Ousmane. There was a smattering of applause from the Borussia end.

In the match, Kylian was inspired. He felt something go through him – wanting to give it his best to show that soccer was king, not some mindless, mad violence.

He scored one goal with his knee in a frantic goal-mouth scramble. Then he pulled a trick he had been working on. Taking the ball close to the box, he wriggled free of the defense and faced off against Roman Bürki at the goal. It was as if they were on the training ground. Looking the German keeper in the eye, he paused, then curled the ball unstoppably into the top of the net.

In Monaco, in the Cap d'Ail apartment, Ethan cheered. Then, as his brother slid endlessly on his knees in celebration, arms crossed over his chest, he jumped off the sofa and bounced around the room.

"He did it! He did it!"

This time, it was Ethan's turn to think things were as good as they get.

The TV channels only wanted to talk to Kylian after the game. He gave Ethan the credit for the new celebration, which only made his little brother gawp the more back home. Then he turned to the camera and talked about the bombing.

"Everyone on our team is with the Dortmund players and families tonight. We are brothers. We are footballers. No one should go in fear, just for playing a game."

Everyone fell in love with him.

CHAPTER TWENTY-ONE

The First Cup

All the Monaco team ran out onto the pitch with their faces alive. They were on the brink.

Juventus had knocked them out of the Champions League in the semi-finals – but no one blamed them. They'd had an amazing run, coming up through the qualifying rounds and surpassing every expectation.

Paris Saint-Germain had taken the League Cup from them after a listless performance in the Lyon final. That did make the team angry.

But today, they could get their revenge and take the League One title away from the Parisians, who'd been champions four years running. All they needed was a draw.

Kylian wasn't self-centered enough to think that it was down to him – though, as the season had gone on he'd played a bigger and bigger part in Monaco's games, both on and off the field. The frustration of his lay-off at the beginning of the season seemed far in the past. He was the darling of the supporters, and the darling of the media. He enjoyed the praise – who wouldn't? But what mattered most was that he was held fast in the arms of the team. He was not even halfway through his eighteenth year, and they looked after him.

This match was at home, against St. Etienne F.C. The Louis II stadium was a mass of red, white, and black. The Crown Prince himself, a massive fan, was up in the stands. The sun was shining.

Kylian glanced to his right as he took his position on the pitch. The League One trophy was actually there, on the sidelines, perched on a pedestal, ready to be presented.

You couldn't get a bigger incentive.

As Kylian keyed himself up, waiting for the kick-off, a thousand thoughts went through his head. He put them all in a box and focused on the game. He was going to do his job. He was going to make a difference.

At last, the whistle blew.

Monaco played with verve, the kind of attacking panache that Kylian loved. On the half-hour, it all came together.

Falcao played Kylian through the middle – and it was on. Like lightning, he left two defenders in his wake, then dummied the Saint Etienne keeper to the ground.

It was an open goal.

Kylian planted the ball calmly in it.

The bedlam increased further when Valère Germain bagged a second.

At the final whistle, the team went berserk. Mendy led everyone in a mass dance and sing-song, bowling Leonardo Jardim over as the manager tried to look serious in his press conference.

"Rugrat," Mendy shouted. "Come on! It doesn't get any better!"

It was true, and he joined in. But for him, it was a beginning.

In the dressing room, they made plans for a big night out. The nightclubs of Monaco were legendary and, tonight of all nights, they would be legendary too.

"You coming, Rugrat?" Mendy said. "It'll be a blast."

Kylian thought about it. In the end, he shook his head. "I'll stay with my family. I can't take it in yet!"

Mendy just smiled and ruffled his hair. "Take care, Rugrat."

After everyone left the stadium, he found Mom, Dad, Uncle Pierre, and Ethan. He took them out onto the pitch as the light dimmed. Ethan went sliding all over the grass, doing the celebration over and over. Kylian gazed around the stands in silence, the adults looking on.

Slowly, it sank in. Twenty-six goals in just over half a season.

A League One champion, in his first full season.

For a boy from Bondy, it was pretty good. Yes. It was an achievement.

Suddenly, he knew what he really wanted to do to celebrate.

"I want to take the trophy to Bondy," he said. "I want to show everyone there what's possible. Do you think they'll let me?"

As usual, it was Uncle Pierre who piped up first. "They'd better! The title wouldn't be theirs without you."

Kylian said nothing. He got out his phone.

"Mr. Jardim? Mbappe here. Do you think we could parade the trophy in Bondy? It would mean everything to the kids."

He waited with bated breath. What was he thinking? He was hardly more than a kid himself.

Jardim's voice came gruffly down the line. "Kylian, that's a beautiful idea. I'll see what I can do."

Only a few days later they were all there – Mendy, Falcao, Bayakoko – his friends and colleagues. The open-top bus moved slowly down Bondy's main drag, festooned in white and red. Kylian stood on the top deck, next to the trophy.

In the crowd, he recognized Mr. Kembo the grocer, the neighbors from their first apartment, and so many others. Théo and Fanfan, of course, were in the bus with him, Jirès too.

They took the trophy to the Bondy grounds, where Mayor Sylvine Thomassin introduced him and he made a little speech about working hard. Afterward, it seemed that every family and kid in town wanted a selfie with him and the cup. His face ached from smiling, but he embraced it. Seeing the joy and the ambition lighting the people around him meant everything to him.

When it was over and the cup was put away, he went back to the house that they still kept. It was just the family, plus the neighbors. They toasted him with wine.

He went into the garden after they all went to bed.

Eighteen, and a champion.

The next day he woke up to the news. His beloved club – Paris Saint-Germain – had given him an offer that was so huge he couldn't comprehend it at first. For Kylian, it was a dream come true. Not the money. Just the sheer pleasure of becoming a PSG player. Overnight, he became the most expensive teenager the soccer world had ever seen. PSG was paying a mind-blowing $210 million, not including bonuses, to have him on their roster.

Everything was happening so fast. He was happy, but focused and modest. He knew it was only the beginning of the journey. He still had a lot to prove.

CHAPTER TWENTY-TWO

The Golden Boy

The French national team doctor looked worried when he saw the X-rays. He glanced at Coach Deschamps soberly and said, "Unfortunately Kylian has displaced three vertebrae in his back."

The French national coach's face darkened. Kylian jumped in. "Coach, I can do it. I can play. It doesn't hurt me." An hour ago, he had been picking up his things in the changing room on his way to the shower when he felt as if something in his back was cracking. He couldn't move his back for a few scary minutes. He was shivering with pain. *I hope it's not really bad,* he prayed silently when he went to the doctor and told him what had just happened. He could still feel the pain but he wasn't ready to miss out on the semi-finals of the biggest soccer competition in the world. And he couldn't envision himself being benched when there were only two more games.

His coach wasn't ready either. "Can he play?" he asked the doctor.

The doctor nodded and said, "He can do it."

Deschamps wasn't so sure, but he smiled deep inside. He looked straight into Kylian's eyes and thought about it for a long minute. "OK, we have three days before the semi-finals against Belgium and we'll take the time to rest you and bring you to maximum fitness." He lowered his voice as if he didn't want anyone to hear him. "But one thing must be clear. Nobody outside this team should know that you are injured, because if the opponent's players know how vulnerable you are, they'll try to get you out of the game by targeting the sensitive area in your back. Just a simple shove could send you out to the locker room."

Kylian nodded and smiled broadly. "I'll be ready, Coach. And I'll keep my mouth shut."

In May 2018, he was called to the national team's squad that was headed to the World Cup in Russia. He was part of their qualifying campaign and there was no surprise there. When he was on the pitch, no one seemed to care that he was so young. There was always something mature about him. And the other players loved him. He was sure they were going to win the World Cup. Some people in France accused him of being arrogant because he was confident that France would triumph in Russia. But Kylian was speaking his mind because he truly believed in himself and his teammates. In an interview, he said, "Being honest, it was in my mind for some time. For me, from the beginning, I was convinced that we had everything that we needed to go all the way."

And he was right. He went on to score his first World Cup goal in France's win over Peru and became the youngest French goal-scorer in World Cup history at age nineteen. He continued to dazzle the world when they won 4-3 against Argentina. He scored twice against Messi and a bunch of the world's best players and became the man of the match and the second teenager ever to score two goals in a World Cup match.

The first had been Pelé.

Pelé congratulated him not once but twice. He did it again after the final, where Kylian scored a goal with a stunning 25-yard strike against Croatia. It was a thing of beauty. France won four-two, and Kylian became the second teenager, after Pelé, to score in a World Cup Final. He scored four goals in the tournament and received the FIFA World Cup Best Young Player Award.

Pelé posted on Twitter after the game: *Welcome to the club Kylian,* and Kylian thanked the biggest player ever for his kindness.

The joy of winning the World Cup after twenty years since their win in 1988 swept the French people like a hurricane. The entire country went wild. The players became heroes. Every kid knew their names. They made history, and everyone wanted to wrap them in love and gratitude. Kylian became a household name not only in France but all over the world.

At the medal ceremony, French President Emmanuel Macron stood silently hugging Mbappe tight, seemingly on the verge of tears. More than a million people poured into the streets of Paris, jamming the vast Avenue des Champs-Élysées.

Kylian couldn't grasp what had happened until the team rode through the screaming crowds in an open-top bus the next day. Only then did he realize that he was a part of a team that had left a mark on history.

Up the side of one Bondy high-rise, Nike had erected a billboard of Kylian before the World Cup, referring to France's previous World Cup win in 1998. It read: *'98 was a great year for French football. Kylian was born.* A separate billboard covered eleven floors of a Bondy apartment block for months, depicting him with his thumbs up, and reading: *Bondy: City of Possibilities.*

Kylian never forgot his neighborhood. He donated his World Cup earnings of about $500,000 to a local charity teaching sports to sick and disabled children.

Bondy was where it had all started. Where he had learned to be a soccer player. Bondy is a city that breathes soccer. Where kids are playing and dreaming to become pro-footballers one day. Like Kylian. Their hero.

Kylian knows deep in his heart that it was his upbringing and his loving family that made him who he is. His mom, Faiza had always told him that to become a great football player, you must be, before all, a great man.

And every day he strives to be just that.

THE WORLDS #1 BEST-SELLING SOCCER SERIES!

The Amazing Story of Leo
Messi

THE FLEA

Michael Part

Cristiano
Ronaldo
The Rise of a Winner

Michael Part

Neymar
The Wizard

Michael Part

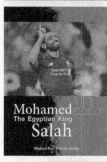

Mohamed
The Egyptian King
Salah

Michael Part & Kevin Ashby

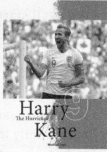

Harry
The Hurricane
Kane

Michael Part

Luis
Suarez
A Striker's Story

Michael Part

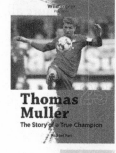

**Thomas
Muller**
The Story of a True Champion

Michael Part

Eden Hazard
The Wonder Boy

Michael Part

**Antoine
Griezmann**
The Kid Who Never Gave Up

Michael Part & Steve Berg

James
The Incredible
Number 10

Michael Part

Balotelli
The Untold
Story

62032331R00069